WJEC GCSE
ADDITIONAL
Science

Jeremy Pollard
Adrian Schmit

HODDER
EDUCATION
AN HACHETTE UK COMPANY

Although every effort has been made to ensure that website addresses are correct at time of going to press, Hodder Education cannot be held responsible for the content of any website mentioned. It is sometimes possible to find a relocated web page by typing in the address of the home page for a website in the URL window of your browser.

Risk Assessment

As a service to our users, a risk assessment for this text has been carried out by CLEAPSS and is available on request to the publishers. However, the publishers accept no legal responsibility on any issue arising from this risk assessment. Whilst every effort has been made to check the instructions of practical work in this book, it is still the duty and legal obligation of schools to carry out their own risk assessments.

Orders: please contact Bookpoint Ltd, 130 Milton Park, Abingdon, Oxon OX14 4SB. Telephone: (44) 01235 827720. Fax: (44) 01235 400454. Lines are open 9.00–17.00, Monday to Saturday, with a 24-hour message answering service. Visit our website at www.hoddereducation.co.uk

First published in 2012 by
Hodder Education
An Hachette UK Company,
338 Euston Road
London NW1 3BH

Impression number	5	4	3	2	
Year	2016	2015	2014	2013	2012

Cover photo Gavin Kingcome/Science Photo Library

Illustrations by Barking Dog Art

Typeset in ITC Legacy Serif Book 11.5pt by DC Graphic Design Limited, Swanley Village, Kent.

Printed in Dubai

A catalogue record for this title is available from the British Library.

ISBN 978 1 444 124347

Contents

Acknowledgements

The Publisher would like to thank the following for permission to reproduce copyright material:

p.52 Figure 5.10, redrawn from *http://info.cancerresearchuk.org/cancerstats/types/lung/riskfactors/#smoking*, reproduced by permission of Cancer Research UK; **p.66** DEFRA, Figure 7.4, 'U.K. Biodiversity indicators in your Pocket 2010', redrawn from *http://jncc.gov.uk/pdf/BIYP_2010.pfd*; **p.119** Figure 11.15, 'Rates of Reaction' from *Focus on Science Investigations 1 software program*, by courtesy of Focus Educational Software Ltd; **p.149** Website quote from *http://improving-your-life.com/230/hard-water-health-benefits-discover-the-secrets-to-why-it-may-improve-life-expectancy*; WHO, extract from Guidelines for drinking-water quality, 2nd ed., Vol.2 from *Health criteria and other supporting information* ; **p.206** 'Speed cameras switched on again', article adapted from *http://www.pressassociation.com/component/pafeeds/2011/04/01/speed_cameras_switched_on_again?camefrom=home* (Wednesday, 17 August, 2011), reproduced by permission of The Press Association.

Photo credits
p.4 CALLALLOO CANDCY – Fotolia; **p.5** Jeffrey Banke – Fotolia; **p.7** Peter Nicholson/Getty Images; **p.9** *l* yukosourov – Fotolia, *m* © amana images inc./Alamy, *r* © Comstock Images/Getty Images; **p.12** TopFoto; **p.13** *tl* © 2008 Nancy Nehring/istockphoto.com, *tr* © Science Photo Library/Alamy, *b* David Becker/Getty Images; **p.18** Cordelia Molloy/Science Photo Library; **p.20** Eye of Science/Science Photo Library; **p.23** J. L. Carson, Custom Medical Stock Photo/Science Photo Library; **p.30** *l* © Chad Ehlers/Alamy, *r* Claude Nuridsany & Marie Perennou/Science Photo Library; **p.42** Michael Steele/Getty Images; **p.47** Oxford Scientific/Photolibrary; **p.51** Dr. Edwin P. Ewing, Jr.; **p.52** NIBSC/Science Photo Library; **p.60** Eye of Science/Science Photo Library; **p.65** *l* FLPA/Mark Sisson, *r* Imagebroker/FLPA RF; **p.67** *l* Olympixel – Fotolia, *r* © Gary K Smith/Alamy; **p.68** Martyn F. Chillmaid; **p.69** © The Photolibrary Wales/Alamy; **p.70** © david tipling/Alamy; **p.72** FLPA/Nigel Cattlin; **p.73** *t* © Imagestate Media (John Foxx), *b* Loke T. Kok, Virginia Polytechnic Institute and State University, Bugwood.org; **p.82** Martyn F. Chillmaid; **p.83** Martyn F. Chillmaid; **p.84** *from t to b* Martyn F. Chillmaid, Martyn F. Chillmaid/Science Photo Library, Andrew Lambert Photography/Science Photo Library, © Phil Degginger/Alamy, © Lester V. Bergman/CORBIS; **p.85** *all* Martyn F. Chillmaid; **p.86** Noel Toone/Photographers Direct; **p.89** *all* Martyn F. Chillmaid; **p.91** *both* Martyn F. Chillmaid; **p.92** sciencephotos/Alamy; **p.98** *tl* adimas – Fotolia, *tr* Windsor – Fotolia, *mr* Igor Kali – Fotolia, *bl* © Wildlife GmbH/Alamy, *br* Tyler Boyes – Fotolia; **p.99** *t* demarco – Fotolia, *m* © Reven T.C. Wurman/Alamy, *b* © stargatechris/Alamy; **p.100** © Wildlife GmbH/Alamy; **p.103** *l* dkimages – Fotolia, *m* adimas – Fotolia, *r* © Can Balcioglu – Fotolia.com; **p.104** *l* Igor Kali – Fotolia, *r* Tyler Boyes – Fotolia; **p.107** Doug Pensinger/Getty Images; **p.108** *t* © 2009–2011 Sarina Fiero, *bl* Yoshikazu Tsuno/AFP/Getty Images, *br* © Phil Degginger/Alamy; **p.109** Pascal Goetgheluck/Science Photo Library; **p.111** © Leslie Garland Picture Library/Alamy; **p.116** choucashoot – Fotolia; **p.117** Eisenhans – Fotolia; **p.136** © Richard Heyes/Alamy; **p.137** Andrew Lambert Photography/Science Photo Library; **p.138** © Mark Lawson/Alamy; **p.140** Ben Stansall/AFP/Getty Images; **p.143** Charles D. Winters/Science Photo Library; **p.145** © Mikael Karlsson/Alamy; **p.147** Sheila Terry/Science Photo Library; **p.150** Phototake Science/Photolibrary; **p.152** © Francisco Martinez/Alamy; **p.165** *l* imagebroker.net/FLPA, *r* Abbas Hasnain/Photographers Direct; **p.169** *from t to b* Axel Schmies/Photolibrary, Neale Haynes/Rex Features, eVox Productions LLC/Photolibrary, © Drive Images/Alamy, www.carphoto.co.uk, © James Leynse/Corbis; **p.176** *t* NASA Nov. 25, 2009, *bl* NASA/Tony Gray, Tom Farrar March 15, 2009, *br* NASA/Bill Ingalls; **p.179** © NASA/Reuters/Corbis; **p.183** NASA; **p.184** NASA; **p.186** *t* NASA, *m* NASA, *bl* NASA, *br* NASA/Bill Ingalls; **p.187** NASA; **p.189** Franck Fife/AFP/Getty Images; **p.190** *t* © Richard Wareham Fotografie/Alamy, *b* Graham Stuart/AFP/Getty Images; **p.191** Andy Hooper/Jamie Mcphilimey/Rex Features; **p.193** *t* Stu Forster/Getty Images, *in table from t to b* Stu Forster/Getty Images, Stu Forster/Getty Images, Mike Hewitt/Getty Images, David Rogers/Getty Images; **p.195** David Rogers/Getty Images; **p.197** © Richard Wareham Fotografie/Alamy; **p.198** © Colin Underhill/Alamy; **p.200** © Alvey & Towers Picture Library/Alamy; **p.201** © DBURKE/Alamy; **p.204** *l* © Hugh Threlfall/Alamy, *r* © SHOUT/Alamy; **p.205** *t* Motoring Picture Library/Alamy, *b* © Alvey & Towers Picture Library/Alamy; **p.207** Pavel Vorobyev – Fotolia; **p.208** *t* TRL LTD./Science Photo Library, *bl* © F1online digitale Bildagentur GmbH/Alamy, *br* © Art Directors & TRIP/Alamy; **p.210** Derek Knottenbelt; **p.211** *tl and tr* Derek Knottenbelt, *b* © World History Archive/Alamy; **p.214** © Bildagentur-online/Alamy; **p.216** *l* Oulette & Theroux, Publiphoto Diffusion/Science Photo Library, *r* Beranger/Science Photo Library; **p.217** © Sergio Azenha/Alamy; **p.218** © Steve Morgan/Alamy; **p.219** Lasse Kristensen – Fotolia; **p.220** GAMMA/Gamma-Rapho via Getty Images; **p.221** KeystoneUSA-ZUMA/Rex Features; **p.227** *t* Patrick Aventurier/GAMMA/Getty Images, *b* SOHO/ESA/NASA; **p.229** EFDA-JET/Science Photo Library.

t = top, *b* = bottom, *l* = left, *r* = right, *m* = middle

Introduction

This book has been produced to complement the new GCSE Additional Science specification which is to be taught from September 2012. Although much of the content remains the same, the new course, and therefore this book, places much greater emphasis on 'How Science Works', and exam candidates will also be expected to be able to clearly explain scientific concepts. Many of the exercises in the book are designed to develop and test these abilities.

'How Science Works'

This term includes an understanding of the methods scientists use to investigate problems, involving experimental design, risk assessment, careful measurement, presentation and analysis of results, and the evaluation of methods used. It also involves an understanding of how original ideas become accepted theories, or are rejected as a result of new evidence. Ethical issues need to be considered, too, as science becomes capable of doing things that some people find unacceptable for moral rather than scientific reasons. The exercises and questions in this book focus very much on scientific enquiry skills and general aspects of 'How Science Works'.

Communication skills

Communication is vitally important in the scientific community. It is no good being able to understand the nature of (or answer to) a scientific problem if you cannot clearly explain it to others. Public misunderstandings of some scientific issues have resulted from the facts being poorly explained either by scientists themselves or by the media. In the new Science GCSE, candidates are to be tested on their communication skills and it will no longer be enough to just know the facts. The exams will contain questions that require extended writing, and there are exercises in the book which provide opportunities to develop and practise such skills.

How to use this book

The subject content of the new WJEC Additional Science GCSE is fully covered, both at Foundation and Higher level. In addition, there are numerous exercises which fall into the following categories:

Practical work

Practical exercises have been chosen to help the understanding of concepts, but also include questions which focus on the scientific enquiry skills which are so important for success at GCSE.

Tasks

The tasks are exercises that usually involve the use of second hand information and data that could not be obtained in a school laboratory, along with questions that consider such things as experimental design, analysis of data and judgements about the strength of evidence.

Questions

Questions are scattered throughout the book to test understanding and application of concepts. We have not included past exam paper questions, for reasons of space but also because the exam papers for the new specification will look rather different from those of the past. It is possible to download past papers, if required, from the WJEC website.

Discussion points

Discussion points are questions that could be answered by individuals, but that benefit from discussion with others, either in peer groups or led by the teacher. In such cases there are usually a variety of opinions or possible answers.

For teachers

Guidance and support materials for teachers whose classes are using this textbook can be found on the WJEC website at http://www.wjec.co.uk/sciencegcse.

Tiering

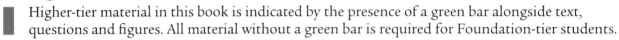 Higher-tier material in this book is indicated by the presence of a green bar alongside text, questions and figures. All material without a green bar is required for Foundation-tier students.

Developing scientific enquiry skills

What should I already know?

The following enquiry skills were covered in the GCSE Science textbook and will not be covered in this chapter:

- asking scientific questions
- fair testing
- accurate measurement
- judging how many repeats to carry out
- deciding how to present results as tables and graphs
- communication skills
- risk assessment.

These skills were covered in the GCSE Science textbook and will be developed further here:

- designing experiments to test hypotheses
- analysing results
- judging the strength of evidence.

These new skills will be covered:

- devising scientific hypotheses
- drawing conclusions
- evaluating experimental methods.

What is a hypothesis?

Scientists try to explain the world around us. They make observations and try to explain them, using the available evidence. A suggested explanation is called a **hypothesis**. A hypothesis is more than just a guess, because it can be justified by scientific evidence and/or previous knowledge. A hypothesis is not the same as a prediction, but it can be used to make a prediction. A prediction suggests what will happen, but does not explain why, whereas a hypothesis does provide an explanation.

There is no point suggesting a hypothesis if you cannot get any information about whether it is right or wrong, so a scientific hypothesis must be able to be tested by experiment. When scientists do experiments to test a hypothesis, the results can provide evidence that supports or contradicts it. Experiments are generally designed to try to disprove a hypothesis, and sometimes they do. Even if the results do support the hypothesis, it does not *prove* it. If a hypothesis is so well supported by evidence that it is generally accepted, it becomes known as a **theory**.

In summary, a scientific hypothesis:

■ is a suggested explanation for an observation
■ is based on evidence
■ can be tested by experiment.

QUESTIONS

1 Jane's mum says that she often gets indigestion when she drinks white wine, but not when she drinks red wine. Jane, Aaron, Dave and Rebecca are suggesting hypotheses to explain why.

JANE
Wine is acidic and indigestion is caused by too much acid in your stomach. Perhaps white wine is more acidic than red.

DAVE
Wines are not all the same strength of alcohol. Perhaps the white wine is just stronger in alcohol than the red.

Aaron
I think that as people get older they can't drink as much alcohol without showing side effects. Jane's mum is 48.

REBECCA
My mum prefers red wine too. Maybe white wine just upsets your stomach more.

Figure 1.1 Suggested hypotheses for Jane's mum.

For each person, say:

a If the suggestion qualifies as a scientific hypothesis and
b If it does, say whether you think it is a *good* scientific hypothesis.
2 Explain the differences between a hypothesis, a prediction and a theory.

How do you devise a hypothesis?

Scientists have to be able to suggest hypotheses to explain things that they observe, so that they can test them with experiments to find out how and why things happen in the world around them.

We have seen in the previous section that there are a number of criteria for a hypothesis.

You actually make hypotheses all the time in everyday life to solve problems. Let's look at an example. You go to use a torch, and find it doesn't work. You immediately make one or more hypotheses (see Figure 1.2).

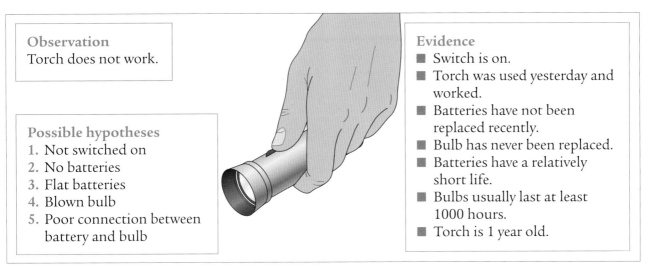

Observation
Torch does not work.

Possible hypotheses
1. Not switched on
2. No batteries
3. Flat batteries
4. Blown bulb
5. Poor connection between battery and bulb

Evidence
- Switch is on.
- Torch was used yesterday and worked.
- Batteries have not been replaced recently.
- Bulb has never been replaced.
- Batteries have a relatively short life.
- Bulbs usually last at least 1000 hours.
- Torch is 1 year old.

Figure 1.2 Hypotheses for torch not working.

We must now consider the five hypotheses we have thought of.

Table 1.1

	Hypothesis	Evidence	Accept/reject	Can it be tested?
1	Not switched on	Switch is on.	Reject	No need
2	No batteries	Torch was used yesterday and it is unlikely batteries would have been removed since (but not impossible).	Accept	Yes (look to see if there are batteries inside)
3	Flat batteries	Batteries have not been replaced recently and batteries have a limited life.	Accept	Yes (replace batteries)
4	Blown bulb	Bulb has never been replaced but is well within its life span.	Accept	Yes (replace bulb)
5	Poor connection	No evidence either for or against.	Accept	Yes (inspect and clean contacts)

We now have four hypotheses, all of which can be tested. Looking at the strength of the evidence, hypothesis 3 (flat batteries) seems the most likely, and would be easy to test. In looking to replace the batteries, you would also be testing hypothesis 2. If you replace the batteries and the torch still does not light, you would reject hypothesis 3 and go on to test hypothesis 4 or 5.

You do this sort of thing often – you just may not have known that you were developing a hypothesis!

This activity helps you with:
★ using evidence
★ constructing a hypothesis
★ designing experiments to test a hypothesis.

Let us look at an observation and see if you can devise a hypothesis to explain it.

Figure 1.3 This dog is waiting at the window for its owner to arrive.

Dogs will often wait by a window or door in their house just before their owner returns home from work. This is an observation that must have some explanation if it happens regularly (which dog owners say it does). You need to devise a hypothesis that will explain this behaviour, and fit with any evidence or scientific knowledge.

Let's start by collecting information about the observation. Mark and Anne have a dog called Prince. Mark drives home from work and arrives around 6 pm. Anne says that around 5.50 pm, Prince sits by the window overlooking their drive and does not move until Mark's car arrives. Prince hardly ever sits by the window at any other time of day.

Evidence and scientific knowledge
- Prince always goes to the window at about 5.50 pm.
- His owner always arrives home about 6 pm.
- Prince does not sit by the window at other times of the day.
- Dogs have much more highly attuned senses of smell and hearing compared to humans.
- All mammals have a **biorhythm** – that is, they are aware of roughly what time of day it is even if they can't read a clock.

Questions
1 Suggest **at least two** possible hypotheses that might explain Prince's behaviour.
2 Pick **one** of your hypotheses and suggest how you might test it.

An experiment with no hypothesis

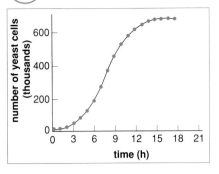

Figure 1.4 Population of yeast cells over time.

Scientists investigating how populations of yeast cells grow over time simply set up a population and counted the cells at different times. They did not have a hypothesis for what was going to happen.

When they got the results shown in Figure 1.4, they then had to think of a hypothesis to explain the curve.

Drawing conclusions – is my hypothesis supported?

Not all experiments test a hypothesis. Some are done with no real idea what will happen – they are actually carefully constructed observations which may lead to a hypothesis. If there is a hypothesis, the purpose of the experiment is to test it, so the conclusions can only be one of three:

1 The evidence supports the hypothesis.
2 The evidence does not support the hypothesis.
3 The evidence is not conclusive either way.

Experiment can very rarely **prove** a hypothesis.

Centuries ago, the people of Europe believed that swans were always white, because every swan they had ever seen was white. They had the hypothesis that 'all swans are white'. In 1697, though, explorers in Australia found black swans (these have since been introduced into Britain). This instantly disproved the hypothesis, because there could be no doubt whatsoever about the evidence. No matter how many white swans the Europeans saw, this would never have proved that all swans are white. Even if black swans had never been discovered, no-one could be certain that there wasn't one somewhere in the world still waiting to be found!

Figure 1.5 This black swan clearly disproves the 'all swans are white' hypothesis.

If a long series of experiments have been carried out and all of them support the hypothesis, then scientists treat the hypothesis as if it was true (it becomes a **theory**) even though they still would not say it had been *proved*.

In order to decide whether to continue to accept the hypothesis or reject it, the strength of the evidence is very important.

The flow chart shown in Figure 1.6 shows how scientists arrive at conclusions about a hypothesis.

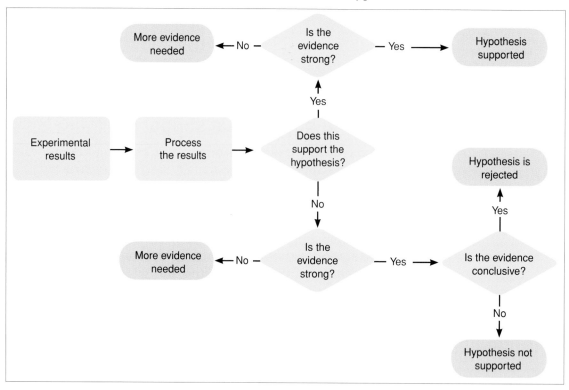

Figure 1.6 Hypothesis decision-making flow chart.

QUESTIONS

3 Natalie had a hypothesis that wet paper could hold less weight than dry paper. She tested paper bags, adding weight 10 g at a time until the bag broke. She tested 10 bags, and then soaked 10 similar bags in water and tested them. In every single case, the wet bags broke with less weight in them than the dry bags. What should Natalie's conclusion be?

a Her hypothesis is proved.

b Her hypothesis is supported.

c Her hypothesis is doubtful.

d Her hypothesis should be rejected.

4 Glyn had a hypothesis that a certain brand of insulated mug did not actually keep drinks any warmer than a normal ceramic mug. He timed how long it took water to cool by 10 °C in the two types of mug. He ran the test 50 times. On average, the water took 6 minutes longer to cool down in the insulated mug, and in all 50 tests the water in the ceramic mug cooled quicker. What should Glyn's conclusion be?

a His hypothesis is proved.

b His hypothesis is supported.

c His hypothesis is doubtful.

d His hypothesis should be rejected.

TASK   CAN PEOPLE TELL THE DIFFERENCE BETWEEN BUTTER AND A BUTTER SPREAD?

This activity helps you with:
★ judging the strength of evidence
★ drawing conclusions
★ assessing a hypothesis.

A number of butter spreads claim to taste 'just like butter'.

Patrick and Isobel did an investigation to find out if people could tell genuine butter and butter spread apart. There is not much real evidence either way for this, but as the producers of butter spread claimed that it was difficult to tell the difference, their hypothesis was 'People cannot tell butter from butter spread'.

They tested a sample of 10 people. Each person was tested 10 times, and on each occasion they tasted the butter and spread on crackers, without knowing which was which, and tried to identify the butter. Each person had to make a decision each time whether they were eating butter or butter spread; they could not say that they did not know.

Patrick and Isobel's results are shown in the table. A tick indicates a correct decision and a cross an incorrect decision.

Figure 1.7 Can she tell if she's eating butter?

Table 1.2 Patrick and Isobel's results.

Person	Results of tests										% correct
	Trial 1	Trial 2	Trial 3	Trial 4	Trial 5	Trial 6	Trial 7	Trial 8	Trial 9	Trial 10	
Patrick	✓	✓	✗	✓	✓	✓	✗	✓	✗	✓	70
Isobel	✓	✗	✓	✓	✗	✗	✓	✓	✓	✗	60
James	✗	✓	✗	✗	✓	✓	✗	✓	✗	✗	40
Amira	✓	✗	✓	✗	✓	✗	✓	✓	✗	✓	60
Belle	✗	✓	✗	✓	✗	✓	✗	✗	✗	✗	30
Dan	✓	✗	✓	✓	✓	✓	✓	✓	✗	✓	80
Becky	✓	✗	✗	✗	✓	✗	✗	✓	✓	✗	40
Ryan	✗	✓	✗	✓	✗	✓	✗	✓	✓	✓	60
Mohammed	✓	✓	✓	✓	✗	✓	✓	✗	✗	✓	70
Ruby	✗	✓	✓	✗	✓	✗	✓	✗	✓	✗	50
Mean											56

1 Patrick and Isobel's hypothesis was 'People cannot tell butter spread from butter'. The alternative is 'People *can* tell butter spread from butter'. Comment on the evidence for each of these hypotheses.

2 What is your conclusion from these results?

How do scientists evaluate their methods?

When scientists get their results, they evaluate the method they used in the light of those results to decide if it was acceptable, or if it needs to be improved. When they are satisfied, they publish their results in scientific journals, so that other scientists can also evaluate their methods and their conclusions.

For a method to be accepted, it has to pass three tests:

1 Was the method **valid**? In other words, did it test the hypothesis it was meant to test?
2 Did the method provide **accurate** results?
3 Did the method give **repeatable** results? This means that there was not much variation between the repeat results.

Notice that this evaluation is of the method itself, not how well it was performed. If scientists feel that they may have made mistakes when carrying out the method, they ignore the results collected and start again.

Validity

A **valid** experiment is one that tests the hypothesis it was designed to test. An invalid experiment is useless and would need to be re-designed. Experiments can be invalid for a number of reasons.

1. It is not a fair test

If the experiment is not fair, then it is not a proper test of the hypothesis. For example, if you want to test the effect of temperature on the rate of reaction of magnesium with hydrochloric acid, but you fail to control the amount of magnesium used, then the method is invalid because the results don't actually test the effect of temperature on its own.

2. The method of measurement is inappropriate

Sometimes, the method used to measure something in an experiment is clearly biased, or inappropriate in some other way. For example, in surveys to measure illegal drug use, many people who have used such drugs will not admit it. If no other tests are used to measure drug use, the results may be so inaccurate that the method is actually invalid. Sometimes, heart rate has been used to measure people's stress level. Many other things apart from stress can cause an increase in heart rate, so this may not produce valid results.

3. The sample size or number of repeats is too small

If results vary quite a lot, then a big sample or a lot of repeats are necessary. Scientists will sometimes repeat their experiments 100 times or more before they can be sure of their results. If a very small sample or number of repeats is used, the experiment is unlikely to lead to valid conclusions.

An invalid method does not necessarily produce incorrect results. It is just that no-one can be certain whether the results are right or wrong, and so the experiment is pointless.

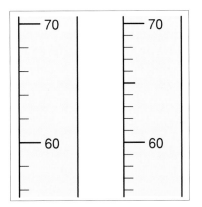

Figure 1.8 The scales on these two measuring cylinders show different resolutions. The one on the right is calibrated every 1 cm³, but the one on the left is only calibrated every 2 cm³, meaning that readings of 61 cm³ or 67 cm³, for example, have to be estimated rather than measured. The measuring cylinder on the right is therefore more accurate. It is accurate to 1 cm³, whereas the one on the left is only accurate to 2 cm³.

Accuracy

A measurement result is considered accurate if it is judged to be close to the **true value**. The problem is that scientists can never know what the 'true value' really is. They can never say for certain that their measurements are accurate, but they can look for possible reasons why they might be **inaccurate**. If there are no such reasons, they will assume that the measurements are accurate. Things that might make results inaccurate include:

■ Difficulty in taking the measurement (e.g. trying to count bubbles, timing a colour change).
■ Poor resolution of the measuring instrument. Resolution was dealt with in Chapter 1 of WJEC GCSE Science.

If results are inaccurate, repeating the measurements does not help.

1. The method of measurement

When designing an experiment, the scientists should choose the most accurate instruments and methods that are available (see Figure 1.8).

The way measurements are taken may also reduce accuracy, if they are likely to lead to error. Some examples are shown in Figure 1.9.

a) If the needle on an analogue dial is not steady, it is difficult to tell the exact reading.

b) When timing a colour change, it is often difficult to tell the exact moment at which the change happened.

c) This stop watch is accurate to 0.01 seconds, but human reaction times are longer than that when pressing the button, so the readings are less accurate.

Figure 1.9

2. Accurate means

The more repeats of an experiment you do, or the bigger the sample you use, the more accurate any mean will be. There will always come a point when taking more readings has such a small effect on the mean, there is no point in continuing.

Let's look at some readings.

> 1, 6, 2, 4, 2, 2, 2, 3, 1, 1, 3, 2, 2, 1, 2,
> 3, 4, 1, 1, 1, 2, 3, 2, 3, 1, 3, 1, 1, 2, 1   Mean = 2.1 (30 readings)

Now look at what happens with the same data when fewer readings are taken.

> 1, 6, 2, 4, 2, 2, 2, 3, 1, 1, 3, 2, 2, 1, 2,
> 3, 4, 1, 1, 1   Mean = 2.2 (20 readings)

> 1, 6, 2, 4, 2, 2, 2, 3, 1, 1   Mean = 2.4 (10 readings)

> 1, 6, 2, 4, 2   Mean = 3.0 (5 readings)

Five readings gives an inaccurate mean because the figure of 6 is clearly a 'rogue' result, and even 4 is slightly unusual, as can be seen from the data from 30 readings. As the number of readings increases, the effect of the rogue result becomes less, and the mean becomes more accurate.

> ## QUESTION
>
> 5 In the experiment described at the bottom of page 9, how many readings do you think the person doing the experiment should have taken?

Repeatability

If you design an experiment that is valid and accurate, there is a good chance that your results will be fairly consistent, i.e. **repeatable**. Repeatable results are ones that do not show much variation. If readings are not repeated at all, you cannot tell whether the experiment gives repeatable results. When there is a wide variation between repeat results, this may indicate a problem with the design of the experiment, and scientists then have to think about if any aspect of the experimental design might have caused that variation.

Sometimes, large variations in results are inevitable, particularly in biology, because living things are so complex. For instance, different people have very different reactions to drinking caffeine, with some being much more sensitive than others. If you study the effects of caffeine on human beings, you are always going to get quite a lot of variation in results. The only thing that can be done is to do a lot of repeats, or have a very large sample so that you can try to see if there is any general trend.

Reproducibility

Reproducibility means that if you (or someone else) did the whole experiment again, you or they would get similar results. If the experiment is valid, and the results are as accurate as possible and don't show too much variation, then it is likely that the experiment is reproducible. You can't be certain of this until the experiment *is* done again.

TASK   ARE YOU A SCIENTIST YET?

This activity helps you with:
★ putting all your scientific enquiry skills together to complete a full scientific investigation.

Below are some observations. Pick one, and devise and test a scientific hypothesis to try and explain it.
- Woodlice tend to be found in dark places.
- It is very important that people notice warning signs. Warning signs are nearly always red.
- Cheap brands of fizzy drinks seem to go 'flat' quicker than more expensive brands.

Chapter summary

- A hypothesis is a suggested explanation for an observation which is based on evidence and can be tested by experiment.
- Evidence can either support or contradict a hypothesis, or may be inconclusive.
- A hypothesis is not a prediction, although it can be used to make predictions.
- A hypothesis can easily be disproved, but can rarely be proved.
- If a hypothesis is supported by lots of evidence and is generally accepted as true, it becomes a theory.
- Scientists evaluate their experiments by deciding if the experiment was valid, and if the results were accurate and repeatable.
- Experiments should also be reproducible, that is, give similar results each time the experiment is done, whoever it is done by.
- Different measuring instruments have different levels of accuracy, linked to their resolution.
- Repeating readings makes means more accurate, and allows repeatability to be assessed.
- The more variable the results are, the more times the experiment needs to be repeated (or the bigger the sample needs to be).

> means?

Cells and cell processes

What are cells?

Figure 2.1 An early microscope used by Robert Hooke to discover cells.

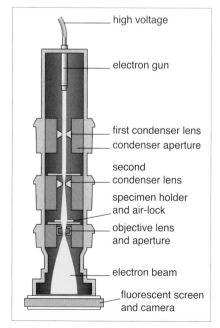

Figure 2.2 An electron microscope. A beam of electrons is shot through the specimen and is detected by a fluorescent screen.

Cells are now known to be the basic 'unit' of all living things. Cells were first described by the famous scientist Robert Hooke in 1665, but at that time he had no idea that cells were found in all living things. That idea, which formed part of what is known as the cell theory, was first suggested by German scientists Theodor Schwann (working on animals) and Matthias Schleiden (who worked on plants) in the 1830s.

The cell theory that Schwann and Schleiden proposed is still the basis of cell theory today, although it has been developed as we have come to know more about cells.

Today's cell theory states that:

1 All living organisms are composed of cells. They may be **unicellular** (one celled) or **multicellular** (many celled).
2 The cell is the basic 'unit' of life.
3 Cells are formed from pre-existing cells during cell division.
4 Energy flow (the chemical reactions that create life) occurs within cells.
5 Hereditary information (**deoxyribonucleic acid, DNA**) is passed on from cell to cell when cell division occurs.
6 All cells have the same basic chemical composition.

Points 1 and 2 were suggested by Schwann and Schleiden. Points 3–6 have been added by later scientists. Like many scientific theories, the cell theory has been modified from time to time as new discoveries are made. Schleiden and Schwann used a light microscope (in other words, you see the image in the microscope because light passes through it). The quality of light microscopes has continually improved, but the properties of light mean that it is impossible to magnify an image by more than × 1000.

In the 1930s, an electron microscope was developed. This uses electrons instead of light, and it is possible to get much larger magnifications – the best modern types can magnify as much as 50 million times. You don't 'look into' an electron microscope, because you can't see electrons. Instead, the image is displayed on a monitor (see Figure 2.2). The disadvantages of electron microscopes are that you cannot see colour, and cannot observe living specimens (because the specimen needs to be processed before it can be viewed).

The pictures produced by an electron microscope allowed scientists to discover the internal structure of cells, seeing features that had been invisible before (see Figure 2.3).

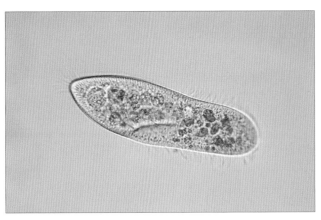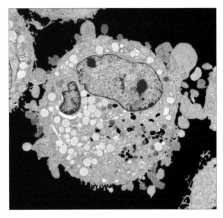

Figure 2.3 Under the light microscope (left), it is clear that the cell contains structures, but these cannot be seen clearly. Under the electron microscope (right) much more detail can be seen, even at relatively low magnification.

A modern development in microscopy is the use of lasers to build up an image via a computer by scanning an object in the microscope. This is known as **confocal laser scanning microscopy**, and highly detailed images can be built up using this technique (see Figure 2.4). While the technique does not produce as high a magnification as electron microscopy, it produces clearer images than light microscopy.

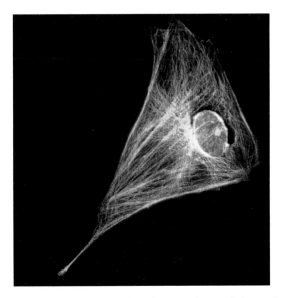

Figure 2.4 Confocal scanning microscopy image of a human bone cell.

Are cells the same in plants and animals?

Cells come in a variety of shapes and sizes, and some look very different from others. However, all cells in plants and animals have certain features in common.

- They all have **cytoplasm**, a sort of 'living jelly', where most of the chemical reactions that make up life go on.
- The cytoplasm is always surrounded by a **cell membrane**, which controls what enters and leaves the cell.
- They have a **nucleus**, which contains DNA, the chemical which controls the cell's activities.

Plant cells can be distinguished from animal cells, though, because they have some features that are not seen in animal cells. These are:

- A cell wall, made of cellulose, which surrounds all plant cells.
- A large, permanent central **vacuole**, which is a space filled with liquid cell sap.
- **Chloroplasts**, which absorb the light plants need to make their food by photosynthesis. Chloroplasts are not found in all plant cells, but are never found in animal cells.

Figure 2.5 shows examples of plant and animal cells, showing the differences.

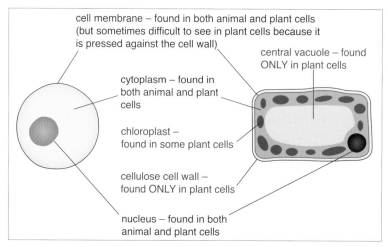

cell membrane – found in both animal and plant cells (but sometimes difficult to see in plant cells because it is pressed against the cell wall)

central vacuole – found ONLY in plant cells

cytoplasm – found in both animal and plant cells

chloroplast – found in some plant cells

cellulose cell wall – found ONLY in plant cells

nucleus – found in both animal and plant cells

Figure 2.5 Examples of animal (left) and plant cells (right) showing differences in structure.

Just like whole organisms, cells have evolved over time to become specialised for their particular 'jobs'. This can sometimes result in cells that look very different from the examples in Figure 2.5 (see Figure 2.6).

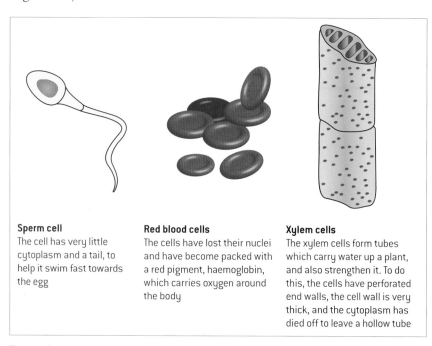

Sperm cell
The cell has very little cytoplasm and a tail, to help it swim fast towards the egg

Red blood cells
The cells have lost their nuclei and have become packed with a red pigment, haemoglobin, which carries oxygen around the body

Xylem cells
The xylem cells form tubes which carry water up a plant, and also strengthen it. To do this, the cells have perforated end walls, the cell wall is very thick, and the cytoplasm has died off to leave a hollow tube

Figure 2.6

PRACTICAL | **CAN YOU FIND CELLS?**

In this activity you will need to prepare slides for looking at under the microscope. The technique is shown in Figure 2.7.

This activity helps you with:
★ using a microscope
★ preparing a slide
★ understanding the link between structure and function in cells.

Procedure

1 Look at ready-prepared slides of various animal and plant cells and tissues.
2 Investigate the cells in a stick of celery.
  a The 'strings' of celery can be pulled off and mounted on a slide. They are made of xylem cells.
  b You can cut very thin sections of the celery stalk and look at them under the microscope.
  c If you rip the celery leaves you may be able to see cells in the thinnest parts near a tear.
3 Lightly rub the inside of your cheek with a cotton wool bud. This will scrape off some surface cheek cells, which are only very weakly attached. Smear the cells onto a slide and mount them using methylene blue stain. If you look carefully under the microscope, you will be able to see your own cells.
4 Research one of the following cells on the internet: phloem cell, white blood cell, leaf palisade cell, human egg cell (ovum). Draw an example, and explain how the cell is suited to its function.

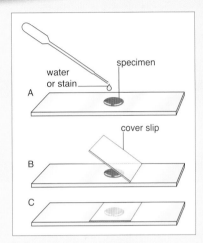

Figure 2.7 Preparing a slide.

Do micro-organisms have cells?

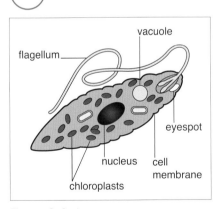

Figure 2.8 *Euglena*.

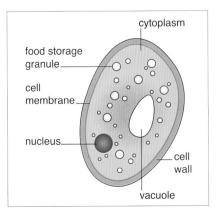

Figure 2.9 Yeast cell.

Micro-organisms come in various types – bacteria, unicellular algae, some fungi, and viruses are referred to as micro-organisms. Viruses don't follow the general pattern, and we will deal with them later, but all the others are made up of one cell.

Protista are single celled organisms, some of which have a structure more like a plant cell, and some more like an animal cell. A protist, *Euglena*, is shown in Figure 2.8. It is an algal cell which shows a mixture of plant and animal cell features. It has chloroplasts, but no cell wall. It also has unusual cell structures like a flagellum (which it thrashes around to swim through the water), an 'eyespot', which can detect light, and a 'contractile' vacuole which helps it to get rid of excess water.

Fungi have cells which are different from animal and plant cells. Yeast is an example of a single-celled fungal micro-organism. The structure of a yeast cell is shown in Figure 2.9. At first sight it looks like a plant cell without chloroplasts, but, although it has a cell wall, this is not made of cellulose, like in a plant cell. (It is actually made of chemicals called chitin and glucans.) Note that some fungi, e.g. mushrooms, are not classed as micro-organisms because they are multicellular.

Bacteria are cells, but there are a number of differences between them and the cells of animals and plants. These differences are summarised in Figure 2.10. It is thought that the first forms of life were probably bacteria.

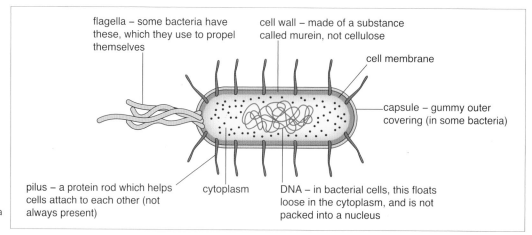

flagella – some bacteria have these, which they use to propel themselves

cell wall – made of a substance called murein, not cellulose

cell membrane

capsule – gummy outer covering (in some bacteria)

pilus – a protein rod which helps cells attach to each other (not always present)

cytoplasm

DNA – in bacterial cells, this floats loose in the cytoplasm, and is not packed into a nucleus

Figure 2.10 Features of a bacterial cell.

Can you call viruses living organisms?

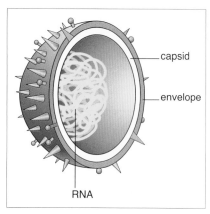

capsid

envelope

RNA

Figure 2.11 Structure of the influenza virus, shown in cross-section.

The cell theory states that all living things are made up of one or more cells. The structure of a virus is so different from the cells we have seen so far that it cannot really be called a cell at all. The structure of the influenza virus is shown in Figure 2.11.

A virus is really just some **nucleic acid** (DNA or the related molecule RNA) in a protein 'package' called a **capsid**. There is no cytoplasm and no cell membrane.

Viruses are even smaller than bacteria, and the first image of a virus was only seen in 1931. Most scientists believe that they are not true living organisms, for the following reasons:

- They can be crystallised. That is more characteristic of chemicals than of living organisms.
- They can only reproduce by using the resources of a host cell.
- They need to be inside a host cell in order to survive – they do not have their own 'metabolism'.

On the other hand, they do have genes, and they can reproduce themselves, even if they need to be inside another living cell to do it. Once they have reproduced, the new viruses are released (which destroys the host cell) and infect other cells. One scientist called them 'organisms on the edge of life', which is probably a good description.

QUESTION

1 The cell theory says that all living organisms are made of cells. Viruses are not made of cells, yet the cell theory is still accepted. Suggest why.

How are the activities of a cell controlled?

All of the activities of a cell depend on chemical reactions, which are controlled by special molecules called **enzymes**. Which enzymes are produced in cells is controlled by another molecule, **deoxyribonucleic acid (DNA)**, which is found in the cell nucleus.

Enzymes

Enzymes are protein molecules that have a particular function. They act as **catalysts**. A catalyst is something which speeds up a chemical reaction. It doesn't react itself, it simply allows the reaction it catalyses to go faster. Here are some important facts about enzymes:

- Enzymes act as catalysts, speeding up chemical reactions.
- Enzymes are specific, which means that a certain enzyme will only catalyse one reaction or one type of reaction.
- Enzymes work better as temperature increases, but if the temperature gets too high they are destroyed (denatured). Different enzymes are denatured at different temperatures.
- Enzymes work best at a particular pH value, but this 'optimum pH' varies in different enzymes.

The chemical or chemicals on which enzymes work are called **substrate(s)**. In order to catalyse a reaction, the enzyme has to 'lock together' with its substrate. The shapes of the enzyme and substrate(s) must match, so that they fit together like a lock and key. That is why enzymes are specific – they can only work with substances that fit with the enzyme's shape.

The action of this 'lock and key' model is shown in Figure 2.12.

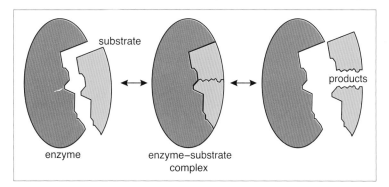

Figure 2.12 The 'lock and key' model of enzyme action. Note that the reaction can go in either direction.

It can be seen from the 'lock and key' model that the shape of the enzyme is important if it is to work. The reason that enzymes won't work if they are at the wrong pH or at too high a temperature is because in these conditions their shape is altered, so that they no longer fit the substrate. Warming an enzyme will actually make it work faster (if the temperature is not so high that it denatures the enzyme), because the enzyme and substrate molecules will move around faster and so will meet and join together more often. We shall learn more about enzymes in Chapter 6.

The part of an enzyme which binds to a substrate is called the **active site** and it is held in shape by chemical bonds. High temperatures and unsuitable pH conditions can break these bonds.

This activity helps you with:

★ designing an experiment (choice of apparatus, validity, fair testing, repeats)
★ drawing conclusions
★ evaluating experimental design.

Enzymes are used for many commercial and industrial purposes, including 'biological' washing powders. Many of the hardest to remove stains are mainly lipid (oils and butter) or protein (blood and grass). The inclusion of enzymes that break down lipids (lipases) and proteins (proteases) in biological washing powders helps to break down these stains. The enzymes used are more resistant to high temperatures than most, but can still be denatured.

Egg yolk is a good stain to test because egg yolk consists mostly of protein with a small amount of lipid. Design and carry out an experiment to test what temperature is best to use with a given brand of biological detergent (in any form). When designing the experiment, consider the following:

- How are you going to 'measure' how successful the detergent has been?
- How are you going to make the test fair?
- How are you going to make sure that you are measuring the effect of the detergent, rather than just the temperature of the water it is in?
- The experiment will not be valid unless the detergent is maintained at more or less its designated temperature throughout the experiment.
- You need to do a risk assessment of your experiment.

Figure 2.13 Biological detergents contain a mixture of enzymes to break down stains.

Work through these questions when you have completed your experiment.

Analysing and evaluating your experiment

1 What is your conclusion from the experiment?
2 How strong is the evidence for your conclusion? Explain your answer.
3 If you could re-design your experiment, is there anything you would now change?
4 What other factors, apart from the effectiveness of stain removal, might influence a decision about what temperature to use for your wash?
5 Explain why enzymes allow washing at a lower temperature than non-biological detergents.

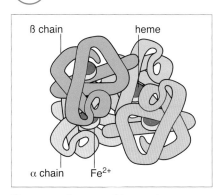

Figure 2.14 Structure of the protein haemoglobin. Each of the different coloured parts is made up of a folded chain of different amino acid molecules. Haemoglobin also has iron molecules (Fe^{2+}) embedded into it. Note that the real molecule is not coloured!

We have already seen that all the chemical activities in cells are controlled by enzymes. Enzymes are proteins, and the 'instructions' for making the enzymes (and other proteins) are stored in the nucleus, in the form of a chemical called DNA (deoxyribonucleic acid).

DNA is the chemical that makes up your genes, controlling the structure and function of your body by controlling the production of proteins. Besides enzymes, other important molecules in the body are made of protein – hormones and antibodies. Proteins are also the main constituents of all the body's tissues (e.g. muscle).

All proteins are made up of long chains of molecules called amino acids. The chains are coiled and folded to give every protein a specific shape, and we have already seen how important this is in enzymes.

DNA contains a sort of chemical code which tells the cell which amino acids to assemble in order to make a protein. DNA is a very strange molecule, because it can make copies of itself. Whenever a new cell is made, it has to have a set of genes, so the DNA duplicates itself and a set of genes is passed into the new cell.

DNA is made up of two long chains of alternating sugar and phosphate molecules connected by pairs of bases. This ladder-like structure is twisted to form a 'double helix' (a helix is a type of spiral). There are four bases in DNA: adenine (A) joins on to thymine (T), and guanine (G) joins on to cytosine (C). The order of these bases along the sugar-phosphate backbone varies in different molecules of DNA. This sequence of bases forms the instructions, in a form of code, for the manufacture of proteins. It determines which amino acids are used to make a given protein, and in what order. The structure of DNA is shown in Figure 2.15.

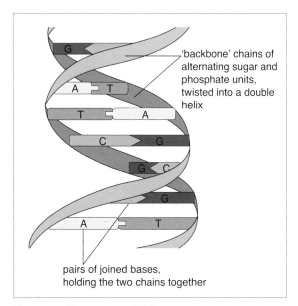

Figure 2.15 The structure of DNA.

The 'code' consists of **triplets** (groups of three) of bases along the DNA. Each triplet codes an individual amino acid in the protein.

Scientists Francis Crick and James Watson are credited with the discovery of the structure of DNA in 1953. This is certainly one of the most important scientific discoveries of all time. It has allowed scientists to identify and analyse genes, and has led to tremendous progress in understanding and treating diseases. However, Watson and Crick did not make this discovery on their own. Other scientists were involved, either directly or by having done preparatory work.

Research the roles the following scientists played in the discovery of DNA:

a) Francis Crick
b) James Watson
c) Rosalind Franklin
d) Maurice Wilkins
e) Linus Pauling.

Discussion Point

Watson and Crick are normally referred to as the 'discoverers' of the structure of DNA. Some people feel that Wilkins and Franklin, in particular, did not receive the credit they deserved. Watson, Crick and Wilkins were awarded the Nobel Prize for the work in 1962, but by that time Rosalind Franklin had died (in 1958). Do you think the credit given to Watson and Crick was fair?

How do new cells form?

A human body has about 50–100 trillion cells in it (depending on size). Yet every human being started out as a single cell inside its mother's body. The cells in the body are constantly being replaced. For example, around 2 million red blood cells are formed (and another 2 million destroyed) every second! All new cells are formed by division of existing cells, as we have already seen in the cell theory. Bacteria actually reproduce themselves by cell division, because they are only one cell big anyway. Yeast cells also reproduce by a form of cell division, known as 'budding' (see Figure 2.16). Because only one cell is involved, this sort of reproduction is asexual (i.e. there is no 'male' and 'female').

Figure 2.16 A yeast cell dividing to form a smaller 'bud' which then grows. The circular marks on the larger cells are scars from earlier budding.

In multicellular organisms, cell division results in growth, and repair and replacement of old or damaged cells and tissues. The type of cell division that occurs in these processes is called **mitosis**, where one cell (the 'mother' cell) divides to form two new ('daughter') cells. The daughter cells are genetically identical to the mother cell. The genes are found on chromosomes, and the number of chromosomes is the same in the daughter cells as in the mother cell. Before dividing, the cell duplicates its chromosomes so that each of the new cells can have a set (see Figure 2.17).

Mitosis is the normal type of cell division, but there is another type. This is called **meiosis**, and it only occurs when sex cells (gametes) are formed. In humans, all the body cells have 46 chromosomes, and mitosis produces new cells with 46 chromosomes. When forming gametes, though, it is important that the sperm and egg cells do not have 46 chromosomes. If they did, when the sperm fertilised the egg, the resulting zygote would have 92 chromosomes, and would not produce a normal human being.

In meiosis, although the DNA and chromosomes duplicate as in mitosis, four new cells are formed instead of two, and each cell receives just half a set of chromosomes. In humans, therefore, the sperm and egg cells each have 23 chromosomes, so that the new baby will have 46 chromosomes as it should. The chromosomes come in pairs which are not identical, and the gametes get one chromosome from each pair. The new cells in meiosis, unlike mitosis, are therefore not genetically identical. Meiosis is shown in Figure 2.18.

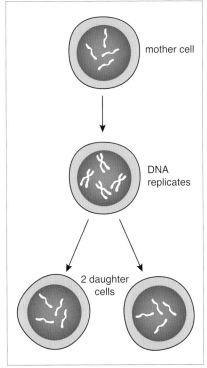

Figure 2.17 Cell division by mitosis.   **Figure 2.18** Cell division by meiosis.

Table 2.1 shows the differences between the two types of cell division.

Table 2.1

Mitosis	Meiosis
Occurs in all body cells EXCEPT those forming gametes	Occurs only in gamete-forming cells
Daughter cells are genetically identical	Daughter cells are genetically different
Two daughter cells are formed	Four daughter cells are formed
Daughter cells have a full set of chromosomes	Daughter cells have a half set of chromosomes

QUESTIONS

2 Cats have 38 chromosomes, dogs have 78 and wheat has 42. How many chromosomes would you expect to find in:

   a an egg cell of a dog?

   b a kidney cell of a cat?

   c a pollen cell of wheat?

3 Why would meiosis not work as the 'normal' method of cell division in the body?

PRACTICAL OBSERVING CELL DIVISION

This activity helps you with:

★ following instructions

★ handling scientific apparatus

★ using a microscope.

In plants, mitosis is concentrated in special growing points in the stems, buds and roots. When the cells are stained with ethano-orcein stain, the chromosomes in dividing cells can be seen. To prepare for this experiment, onions (or garlic cloves) have to be kept with their bases just in contact with water in a beaker, in the dark, for several days (see Figure 2.19). The roots need to be 2–3 cm long.

Apparatus and chemicals

* onion or garlic roots
* ethano-orcein stain
* 1 M hydrochloric acid
* ethanoic alcohol
* watch glass with cover
* microscope slide
* cover slip
* scalpel
* Bunsen burner
* tongs
* dropping pipette
* filter paper
* forceps
* mounted needle
* water bath at 60 °C
* 2 × 100 cm³ beakers
* microscope

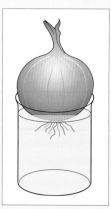

Figure 2.19 Growing onion roots in a beaker of water.

 Risk assessment

You will be provided with a risk assessment by your teacher.

Procedure

1 Cut off about 5 mm of root tips, and place them in a watch glass.

2 Add enough ethanoic alcohol to cover them and leave for 10 minutes.

3 Heat 10–25 cm³ of hydrochloric acid in one of the beakers in the water bath.

4 Place the root tips in a beaker of cold water to wash them for 4–5 minutes and dry on filter paper.

PRACTICAL *contd.*

5 Transfer the tips to the hot hydrochloric acid and leave for 5 minutes.

6 Wash the tips in water again for 4–5 minutes, and dry as before.

7 Place one of the root tips on a microscope slide. Cut the root tip to leave just the terminal 1 mm. Discard the rest.

8 Add a drop of ethano-orcein stain, and leave for 2 minutes.

9 Gently 'mash' the root tip with a mounted needle.

10 Cover the tip with a cover slip.

11 Gently squash the tip by tapping it with the blunt end of a pencil or mounted needle about 20 times. This is best done by dropping the pencil vertically onto the cover slip from a height of about 5 cm.

12 Look at the slide under the microscope and try to find the growing area, where chromosomes will be seen in the cells. See the example in Figure 2.20.

13 Draw two or three dividing cells.

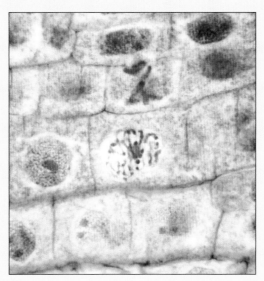

Figure 2.20 Stained onion root cells showing cell division.

Do animals and plants grow in the same way?

In the last activity, you looked at mitosis in plant tissue. It is much easier to find dividing cells in plants than it is in animals, because in animals growth (and therefore cell division) occurs in nearly all tissues. In plants, there are only particular areas (called **meristems**) where growth occurs. These are found in the tips of stems and roots, in buds, and in a special tissue inside stems and roots called the **cambium** (which causes stems and roots to widen).

Plants also have a different pattern of growth to animals. Animals tend to grow to a certain size and then stop growing, whereas plants grow throughout their lives. As plants grow, they branch and spread out, but animals remain compact.

Discussion Points

1 What are the advantages to a plant of a branched growth form? Why might a compact form be better for animals?

2 Why is being able to grow throughout life a particular advantage to plants, and why would it not be so advantageous for animals?

23

Figure 2.21 shows how the growth rate varies in the first 20 years of life of a human.

4 Describe the pattern shown in the graph.

5 Suggest an explanation for the shape of the graph between the ages of 12 and 14.

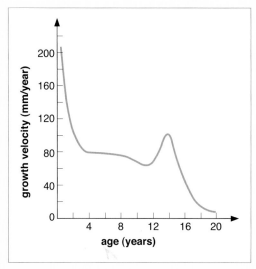

Figure 2.21 Human growth rate from birth to age 20.

What are stem cells?

In the last few years there has been a lot of controversy about the use of stem cells. Stem cells are undifferentiated cells, but what does that mean?

When a plant or animal embryo is formed and starts to grow, the cells all appear the same. Eventually, the cells start to **differentiate** – to become specialised in some way, e.g. a liver cell, a nerve cell, an epidermal cell etc. Once they have differentiated, if they then divide, they can only form similar cells to themselves. A liver cell can never become a nerve cell. The undifferentiated cells in the embryo, though – the stem cells – can become any cell at all. Scientists can take stem cells from an embryo and grow them into types of cells that can be used to repair or replace damaged tissue. This may eventually allow treatment of diseases and conditions such as cancer, type 1 diabetes, brain damage, spinal cord injury and so on. The only trouble is that the embryo, which could grow into a human being, is destroyed in the process. The embryos used for research are from embryos left over after *in vitro* fertility treatment (i.e. the ones not implanted into the mother's womb during a 'test tube pregnancy' treatment), but there is a possibility that embryos could be created purely to supply stem cells, and some people feel that is wrong.

There are alternatives, however. Stem cells can be found in adults (for example, in the bone marrow inside bones). Stem cells can also be collected from the blood from the umbilical cord at birth.

The growing areas of plants, the meristems, also produce cells that can differentiate into other cells (but only cells of that particular plant, so they have no medical use).

TASK — HOW SHOULD WE USE STEM CELLS, IF AT ALL?

This activity helps you with:
★ understanding different opinions about stem cell research
★ making complex judgements about scientific issues
★ understanding how ethical concerns can influence scientific progress
★ judging the strength of evidence
★ practising written communication skills.

Below are some opinions that are held by different people about stem cells. Research stem cells, then pick **one** of the opinions (that you agree with) and write a letter to a newspaper, explaining your opinion and backing it up with evidence.

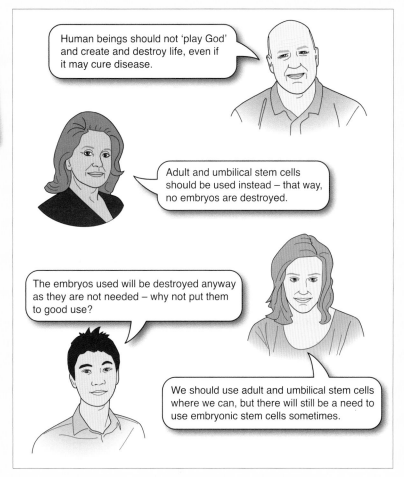

Figure 2.22

Chapter summary

○ The cell theory was first suggested by Schwann and Schleiden and has been developed by other scientists with increasing knowledge.
○ Microbes include bacteria, viruses, fungi and unicellular algae.
○ Bacterial and yeast cells differ in various ways from typical animal and plant cells.
○ Bacteria reproduce asexually by splitting into two.
○ Yeast reproduces asexually by budding.
○ Bacteria may have been the earliest form of life.

○ Animal and plant cells share certain features (nucleus, cytoplasm, cell membrane) but also differ in various ways. Plant cells have a cell wall, a central vacuole and sometimes chloroplasts.

○ Viruses have a simple structure, are smaller than bacteria and can only reproduce inside a host cell. The release of new viruses destroys the host cell.

○ Viruses are not generally considered to be true living organisms.

○ Proteins are composed of a chain of amino acid molecules, folded to form a specific shape.

○ The shape of an enzyme molecule allows it to join with its substrate(s) and so is important for its function.

○ The chemical reactions in cells are controlled by enzymes, which act as catalysts.

○ Each enzyme has its own optimum pH and temperature.

○ Boiling denatures most enzymes by changing their molecular shape.

○ Biological washing powders contain digestive enzymes (lipases, proteases and carbohydrases) which help to break down stains and allow for lower washing temperatures.

○ DNA is made of two long chains of alternating sugar and phosphate molecules, connected by bases. The structure is twisted to form a double helix.

○ There are four bases (A, C, G, T) and the order of these bases forms a code which determines the order in which amino acids are joined together to form different proteins.

○ A number of different scientists collaborated in order to discover the structure of DNA.

○ Cell division by mitosis enables an organism to grow, replace and repair cells.

○ In mitosis, the number of chromosomes remains constant and the daughter cells are genetically identical to the mother cell.

○ Sex cells (gametes) are formed by a different form of cell division called meiosis.

○ In meiosis, the number of chromosomes is halved and the daughter cells are not genetically identical.

○ Mitosis produces two daughter cells, meiosis produces four.

○ Plants and animals have different patterns of growth.

○ Animals usually grow to a finite size, whereas plants tend to grow throughout their life.

○ Plants tend to have a spreading, branched growth form, whereas animals have a compact form.

○ In mature tissues, the cells have usually lost the ability to differentiate into different forms.

○ In both plants and animals, certain cells, called stem cells, are capable of differentiating into different forms of cell.

○ Human stem cells have the potential to replace damaged tissue and could be the basis of treatment for a variety of diseases and conditions.

○ Human stem cells can be obtained from embryos and from adult tissues.

○ Plants have stem cells in their shoot and root tips.

Transport in and out of cells

How do substances get into and out of cells?

In order to get into and out of cells, substances have to get through the cell membrane. The cell membrane is selectively permeable, which means it lets some molecules through but not others. In general, large molecules cannot get through the membrane, but smaller molecules can. Whether they actually do get through, which way they travel, and how quickly, depends upon a number of factors, as we shall see.

There are three processes by which substances move through membranes:

1 **Diffusion**, when molecules sort of 'drift' through the membrane.
2 **Osmosis**, which is a special case of diffusion, involving water only.
3 **Active transport**, when molecules are actively 'pumped' through the membrane in a particular direction.

We now need to consider each of these processes in more detail.

What is diffusion?

Diffusion is the spreading of molecules from an area of higher concentration to an area of lower concentration, as a result of random movement. Molecules are said to move down a **concentration gradient** (see Figure 3.1).

Diffusion is a natural process which results from the fact that all molecules are constantly in motion. It does not require energy. The movement is random – the molecules cannot possibly 'know' in which direction they are heading. The molecules will move in all directions, yet the *overall* (net) movement is always from an area of high concentration to an area of low concentration. Two of the most important substances that enter and leave cells by diffusion are oxygen and carbon dioxide.

The speed of diffusion can be increased by increasing temperature, because the molecules move faster, or by increasing the concentration gradient (the difference between the high and low concentrations).

HIGH CONCENTRATION

molecules travel down the gradient

concentration gradient

LOW CONCENTRATION

Figure 3.1 The 'concentration gradient' concept.

QUESTIONS

1 Why are oxygen and carbon dioxide important in living things?
2 How good a model do you think Figure 3.1 is of diffusion? Is it inaccurate in any ways?

'MODELLING' DIFFUSION

Procedure

1 Place about 10 marbles in a group on the laboratory bench. Ensure that they stay in a group and do not roll apart. These represent molecules in a high concentration. The surrounding areas, with no marbles, represent a low concentration.
2 Bring your fists down firmly on the bench on either side of the group of marbles. This will provide the marbles with energy and they should move. Observe how they travel.
3 You should find that the marbles spread out from the group. In other words, they move from an area of high concentration to an area of low concentration.

This activity helps you with:
★ understanding diffusion
★ interpreting observations
★ developing communication skills
★ judging the accuracy of models.

Questions

1 The marbles never remain in a group, they always spread out. Explain why this happens.
2 In what way(s) is this model an inaccurate way of representing the movement of molecules?

HOW DOES THE CELL MEMBRANE AFFECT DIFFUSION?

This activity helps you with:
★ analysing and interpreting experimental results.

Small molecules can get through the cell membrane, but large molecules cannot. In this experiment, you will be using starch (a large molecule), iodine (a small molecule) and visking tubing, which is a sort of cellophane which has the same properties as a cell membrane. It has pores in it which will let only small molecules through. Iodine stains starch blue-black when it comes into contact with it.

 Risk assessment

Your teacher will provide you with a risk assessment for this experiment.

Procedure

1 Set up the apparatus as shown in the diagram (Figure 3.2). Fill the visking tubing with starch solution using the dropping pipette. Be careful that no starch drips down the outside of the tubing.
2 Place the tube in a test tube rack and leave for about 10 minutes.
3 Observe the result.
4 Explain the colours that you see after 10 minutes inside and outside the visking tubing.

Apparatus
* Boiling tube
* Length of visking tubing, knotted at one end
* Dropping pipette
* Elastic band
* Iodine in potassium iodide solution
* 1% starch solution
* Test tube rack

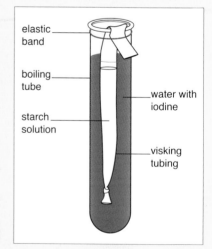

Figure 3.2 Experimental set-up.

Sometimes, you see the cell membrane referred to as 'partially permeable' or 'semi-permeable' rather than 'selectively permeable'. Don't worry – they're all the same thing.

What is osmosis?

Osmosis is a specific type of diffusion. It is the diffusion of **water molecules** through a **selectively permeable membrane**. Diffusion of any other substance through a selectively permeable membrane is just called diffusion. Diffusion of water, but *not* through a membrane, is just diffusion. To be called osmosis, the process has to involve *both* water *and* a membrane.

In osmosis, we say that **water moves from a dilute solution** (which will have more water) **to a concentrated solution** (which will have less water), **through a selectively permeable membrane.**

Notice that the substance (water) which is diffusing is still going down a concentration gradient. A concentrated solution of salt, for instance, would have a low 'concentration' of water, whereas a dilute solution would have a high 'concentration' of water.

The movement of water happens because the membrane is permeable to water (that is, it lets it through), but not to the solute. The process of osmosis is shown in Figure 3.3.

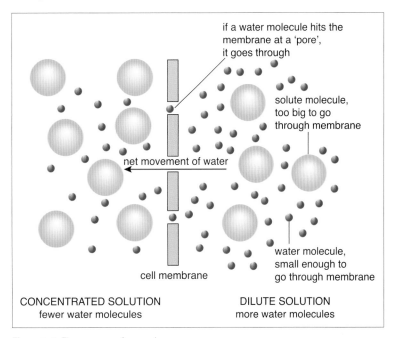

Figure 3.3 The process of osmosis.

All the molecules on both sides of the membrane are moving. Occasionally, a molecule will hit a membrane 'pore'. Water molecules will go through but solute molecules will not. Because there is a higher proportion of water molecules in the dilute solution, more will travel from the dilute solution to the concentrated solution than the other way. Although water molecules move in both directions, there is **net movement** from the dilute to the more concentrated solution.

If the concentrations of the solutions on either side of the membrane are the same, then an equal amount of water will travel in each direction – we say that such solutions are **in equilibrium**.

QUESTION

3 Here are two answers given in an exam. Neither of them got any marks.
   a 'In osmosis, water travels in the opposite way from diffusion, that is, from a dilute solution to a concentrated solution.'
   b 'When the concentrations inside and outside a cell are equal, the movement of water stops.'
   c What is wrong with each of these answers?

Why is osmosis important?

Osmosis is important because too much or too little water inside cells can have disastrous effects. If an animal cell is put into a solution that is more dilute than its cytoplasm, water will go in by osmosis and the cell will burst. If a patient needs extra fluid, they are often put on to a 'saline drip'. Saline is a solution of salts at the same concentration as the blood. If just water was given, the blood would become too dilute and osmosis would make the blood cells burst.

Plant cells are not damaged by being put into water. They swell as water enters, but their cell wall stops them bursting. However, they can be damaged (as can animal cells) by being put into a strong solution. Water will leave the cell by osmosis, and the cytoplasm will collapse and shrink. In plant cells, the cytoplasm pulls away from the cell wall, a condition known as **plasmolysis** (Figure 3.5). Plasmolysis can result in the death of the cell.

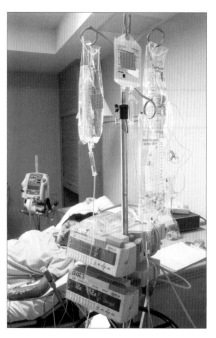

Figure 3.4 Because of the effect of osmosis, this patient is being given a saline solution, not pure water.

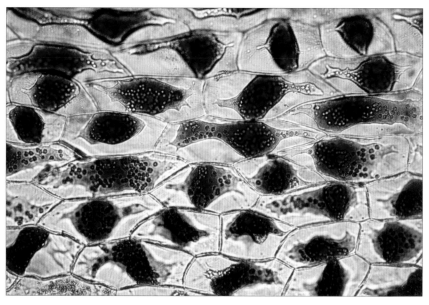

Figure 3.5 These plant cells have plasmolysed. Water has left the cells by osmosis and the cytoplasm has shrunk and pulled away from the cell wall.

OSMOSIS IN POTATOES

In this experiment you will see the changes in potato tissue caused by osmosis. Potatoes are put into different strengths of sugar solution and changes in mass are measured.

Procedure

1. Label the lids of five Petri dishes as shown in Figure 3.6.
2. Into each Petri dish, put 30 cm³ of sucrose solution in the concentration marked on the lid, with distilled water in the fifth dish (see Figure 3.6).
3. Put the lids on the dishes.
4. With a cork borer, carefully cut five cylinders from a potato so that they are each 50 mm long with 5 mm diameter (see Figure 3.7).
5. Weigh this batch of chips accurately on a top pan balance, and record the mass in a table of results.
6. Place these chips in the Petri dish marked distilled water, and put the lid back on the dish.
7. Repeat stages 4–6 for each of the other dishes.
8. Leave the dishes for 20 minutes.
9. Remove the chips from the distilled water. Blot them gently with a paper towel. Weigh them accurately and record the mass in the table of results (Table 3.1).

Apparatus
* 5 Petri dishes
* 100 cm³ measuring cylinder
* Cork borer, 5 mm diameter
* Scalpel
* Potato
* Top pan balance
* Sucrose solutions – 0.1 M, 0.2 M, 0.5 M, 1 M
* Distilled water

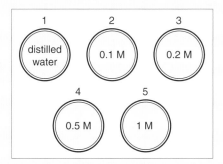

Figure 3.6 Labelled Petri dishes.

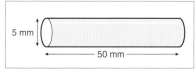

Figure 3.7 A potato cylinder.

Table 3.1

Solution in Petri dish	Mass at start/g	Mass at end/g (after 20 min)	Change in mass/g (+/−)	Change/% (+/−)
Distilled water				
0.1 M sucrose				
0.2 M sucrose				
0.5 M sucrose				
1 M sucrose				

$$\text{percentage change in mass} = \frac{\text{change in mass}}{\text{original mass}} \times 100$$

10. Repeat stage 9 for the chips in the other dishes.
11. Draw a graph of the percentage change in mass against concentration of sucrose. Draw the axes as shown in Figure 3.8.

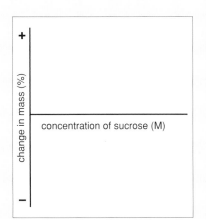

Figure 3.8

continued...

Analysing your results

1 Describe the trend seen in your results, and explain how it was caused.
2 The experiment can also be done by measuring change in length of the potato cylinders. Explain why measuring mass is better.
3 Why was it important to blot the potato cylinders dry before weighing them in step 9?
4 Why were you asked to record % change in mass and plot that in the graph rather than just change in mass?

What is active transport?

Diffusion, and the special form of it called osmosis, both transport substances down a concentration gradient. That is the 'natural' way for molecules to move. Sometimes, though, cells need to get molecules into or out of the cytoplasm against a concentration gradient. In other words, they have to be moved from an area of lower concentration to an area of higher concentration. This will not happen by diffusion, and in order to move the molecules, the cell has to use energy to 'pump' the molecules in the direction they need to go. As this type of transport requires energy, it is called **active transport**.

Comparing active transport, diffusion and osmosis

Figure 3.9 shows the similarities and differences between the three cell transport processes.

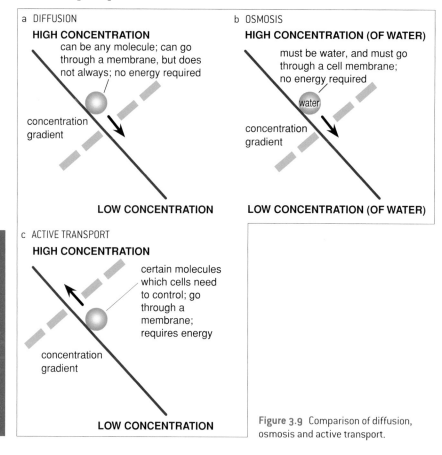

Figure 3.9 Comparison of diffusion, osmosis and active transport.

Chapter summary

- Diffusion is the movement of substances down a concentration gradient.
- Diffusion does not require energy.
- The cell membrane is selectively permeable – it will only let certain substances through.
- The molecules that go through the cell membrane are small molecules; large molecules cannot get through.
- Osmosis is a special form of diffusion, always involving water and always going through a cell membrane.
- In osmosis, there is net movement of water from a dilute solution (high water concentration) to a more concentrated solution (low water concentration).
- Osmosis and diffusion are two-way processes; molecules move in both directions, but more move in one direction than in the other.
- Active transport is used when substances need to be transported against a concentration gradient; this process requires energy.

Photosynthesis and respiration

Photosynthesis and respiration are two of the most basic life processes. All life needs energy, and all life gets that energy by respiration. The source of energy for respiration is food, and food is made, using energy from the Sun, by photosynthesis.

Why study photosynthesis?

Although it only happens in plants, all life on Earth depends upon photosynthesis. It is the process that converts light energy reaching the planet into food, both for plants and for the animals that form the food chains leading from those plants. It also produces oxygen as a waste product, allowing our atmosphere to support aerobic life. Scientists try to understand as much as possible about the process of photosynthesis, in the hope of being able to boost food production for the world's growing population.

What do plants need to survive?

In order to carry out photosynthesis, and their other living processes, plants need certain materials from their environment. Figure 4.1 summarises their needs.

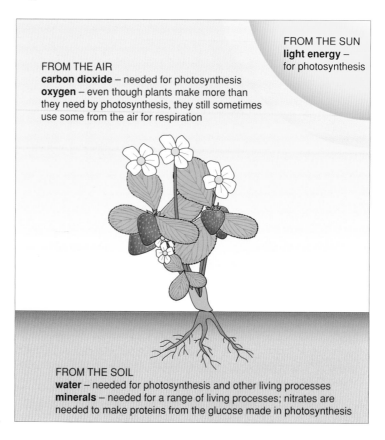

FROM THE SUN
light energy –
for photosynthesis

FROM THE AIR
carbon dioxide – needed for photosynthesis
oxygen – even though plants make more than
they need by photosynthesis, they still sometimes
use some from the air for respiration

FROM THE SOIL
water – needed for photosynthesis and other living processes
minerals – needed for a range of living processes; nitrates are
needed to make proteins from the glucose made in photosynthesis

Figure 4.1 The needs of plants.

How does photosynthesis work?

Photosynthesis is a complex series of chemical reactions in the cells of the plant, but it can be summarised by the following word equation:

$$\text{carbon dioxide} + \text{water} \xrightarrow[\text{light}]{\text{chlorophyll}} \text{glucose} + \text{oxygen}$$

For the process to work, four things are needed:

- **Carbon dioxide**. Glucose is made of carbon, hydrogen and oxygen, and the carbon dioxide provides the carbon and oxygen.
- **Water**. This provides the hydrogen needed to make glucose. The oxygen from the water molecules is not needed and is given off as a waste product.
- **Light**. This provides the energy for the chemical reactions in photosynthesis.
- **Chlorophyll**. The green pigment in chloroplasts is chlorophyll, which absorbs the light to provide the energy for photosynthesis.

All of the chemical reactions involved in photosynthesis are controlled by enzymes, which are available in the cytoplasm of the photosynthesising cells.

PRACTICAL INVESTIGATING FACTORS NEEDED FOR PHOTOSYNTHESIS

This activity helps you with:
- ★ handling apparatus
- ★ understanding the factors necessary for photosynthesis.

For the experiments that follow, we will test whether photosynthesis has occurred in a plant by testing its leaves for starch. Once glucose is made in a leaf, it may be used, transported to other parts of the plant, or stored as starch. For that reason, it is better to look for starch in a leaf, rather than glucose, when testing for photosynthesis.

Starch stains blue-black with iodine solution, but the green colours in a leaf can make it more difficult to see the stain, so first we have to remove the chlorophyll.

Testing a leaf for starch

Apparatus
* Leaf
* Boiling tube
* 250 cm³ beaker
* Bunsen burner
* Heatproof mat
* Tripod
* Gauze
* Forceps
* White tile
* Ethanol
* Iodine solution

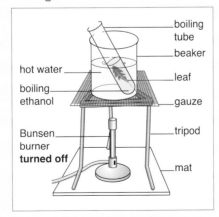

Figure 4.2 Removing chlorophyll from a leaf.

continued...

Risk assessment

Your teacher will provide a risk assessment for this experiment.

Procedure

1 Half fill a 250 cm³ beaker with water. Heat the water with the Bunsen burner to boiling point.
2 Using the forceps, dip the leaf into the boiling water for a few seconds. This kills the leaf and makes it permeable to the chemicals used later.
3 **Turn the Bunsen burner off** (so the ethanol you use in the next stage will not catch alight).
4 Place the leaf in the boiling tube and cover it with ethanol.
5 Place the boiling tube in the beaker of hot water and leave it for 5 minutes. The ethanol should boil, and the leaf will gradually lose colour, turning the ethanol green.
6 Using a test-tube holder, remove the boiling tube from the water bath and pour off the ethanol.
7 Remove the leaf from the boiling tube. An easy way to do this is to fill the tube with water, so that the leaf floats to the top.
8 Spread the leaf on the tile and cover it with iodine. Leave for about a minute.
9 Gently rinse off the iodine. Areas containing starch will now be stained blue-black.

We will now use this technique to investigate the various factors needed for photosynthesis. When doing these experiments, it is important to make sure that any starch detected has been made during the experiment, and was not already there before. To do this, the plants used (with the exception of the variegated plant used for the chlorophyll experiment) are kept in the dark for 48 hours prior to the experiment. In the dark, no photosynthesis can occur, so the plant is forced to use its stored starch for food.

Experiment 1 – Showing the need for light
A leaf from a de-starched plant is partially covered with aluminium foil to prevent light reaching its surface. The plant is then left in the light for at least 24 hours, and the leaf is then tested for starch.

The covered part of the leaf will remain brown, with only the exposed part containing starch and so turning blue-black.

Experiment 2 – Showing the need for chlorophyll
A variegated (green and white) geranium leaf is tested for starch. Starch is only present in the green areas, which contain chlorophyll. The plant should have been kept in a well lit place before the experiment.

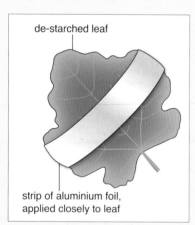

de-starched leaf

strip of aluminium foil, applied closely to leaf

Figure 4.3 Leaf treatment for experiment 1.

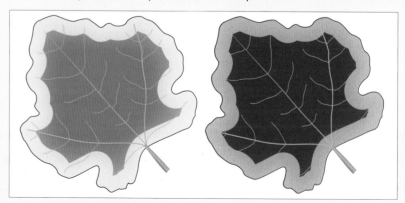

Figure 4.4 Leaf before and after treatment in experiment 2.

PRACTICAL *contd.*

Experiment 3 – Showing the need for carbon dioxide
A de-starched plant is set up in the light for 48 hours, as shown in Figure 4.5. The sodium hydroxide solution absorbs carbon dioxide, so that leaf A is provided with carbon dioxide, but leaf B is not.

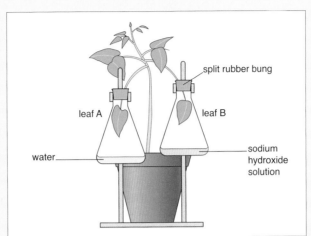

Figure 4.5 Apparatus to test the need for carbon dioxide in photosynthesis.

Test both leaves for starch. Leaf A will contain starch, but leaf B will not.

Questions
1 Why was there no need to de-starch the leaves used for experiment 2?
2 In experiment 3, why was leaf A put in a flask containing water?

Discussion Points

Sodium hydroxide is very corrosive. Apart from any safety hazard, what disadvantage could this be in this experiment? How could this disadvantage be reduced or overcome?

How can we alter the rate of photosynthesis?

Photosynthesis makes food. The more photosynthesis there is occurring in a plant, the more food it makes. Commercial plant growers obviously want photosynthesis to happen as fast as possible in their plants, because that will mean their plants will grow quicker, or be bigger or healthier. If plants are grown in greenhouses, the environmental conditions can be controlled so as to maximise photosynthesis. We know that the external factors needed for photosynthesis are light, carbon dioxide, water and a suitable temperature. So, it would seem logical that the more a plant has of these, the more photosynthesis will occur. However, things are a little more complicated than that.

Light

It is true that increasing light intensity boosts the rate of photosynthesis, but only up to a point. What no-one can alter is the amount of chlorophyll in a plant. If the light intensity is greater than chlorophyll can absorb, then any further increase won't have any effect.

Carbon dioxide

As with light, increasing carbon dioxide levels will increase the rate of photosynthesis up to a certain level, and then increasing it further has no effect. The same argument applies as with light – once the chloroplasts have all the carbon dioxide they need, there is no benefit in increasing it.

Water

Despite the fact that water is needed for photosynthesis, increasing the amount of water a plant has does **not** increase the rate of photosynthesis. Water is needed for much more than photosynthesis in plants, and if there is enough water to keep the plant alive, that will be enough for photosynthesis. Too much water can actually kill plants, as it drives necessary oxygen out of the soil and the roots die off.

Temperature

The chemical reactions in photosynthesis are all controlled by enzymes, and the effect of temperature on the rate of photosynthesis is due to the effect of temperature on those enzymes. Raising the temperature up to about 40 °C is beneficial, as long as you don't dehydrate the plant in the process. As the temperature gets higher, though, it will destroy (denature) the enzymes and photosynthesis will stop.

Limiting factors

In any set of circumstances, one factor is more important than the others in setting the rate of photosynthesis. This factor is known as the **limiting factor**. In different conditions any of the factors listed above, light, carbon dioxide or temperature can be the limiting factor.

WHAT IS THE EFFECT OF INCREASING LIGHT INTENSITY ON THE RATE OF PHOTOSYNTHESIS?

This activity helps you with:
★ understanding the importance of resolution of measurements
★ understanding aspects of experimental design
★ making judgements about the repeatability of results
★ assessing the need for repetition
★ judging the significance of differences
★ drawing conclusions from experimental results.

This experiment was done using leaf discs – small circles cut from the blade of a leaf. They were placed in a syringe containing sodium bicarbonate solution (which provides the carbon dioxide needed for photosynthesis). When photosynthesis occurs, oxygen forms inside the leaf discs and this increases their buoyancy and the discs float to the surface. The apparatus was placed in a dark environment and a lamp was placed at different distances from it (see Figure 4.6). The time taken for 50% of the discs to float to the surface was recorded for each distance. This was used as a measure of the rate of photosynthesis.

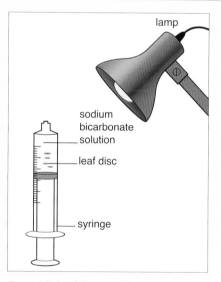

Figure 4.6 Leaf disc apparatus.

The results obtained were as shown in Table 4.1.

Table 4.1 Results table.

Distance of lamp (cm)	Time taken for 50% of discs to float (seconds)			
	Trial 1	Trial 2	Trial 3	Mean
40	848	1029	748	875.0
35	737	788	794	773.0
30	602	628	640	623.3
25	594	588	521	567.7
20	580	530	544	551.3

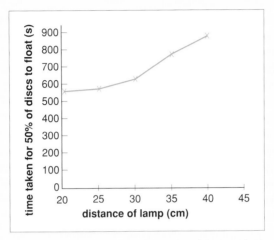

Figure 4.7 Effect of light intensity on rate of photosynthesis – graph of results.

1 Why do you think the time taken for 50% of the leaf discs to float was measured in seconds rather than in minutes and seconds?

2 It was felt that measuring the time taken for 50% of the leaf discs to float would provide a more accurate measure of photosynthesis than waiting for all the discs to float. Why do you think this is?

3 Do you think the variation in the results is acceptable to draw a conclusion from? Explain your answer.

4 Do you think three repeats for this experiment is enough? Explain your answer.

5 Do you think that the differences in the results for the different distances are significant? Explain your answer.

6 What conclusion would you draw from these results?

What happens to the glucose made by photosynthesis?

Just like animals, plants need a balanced 'diet', with a variety of nutrients. The difference is that they have to make the nutrients themselves, apart from minerals which are absorbed from the soil. They need a variety of carbohydrates and proteins. They have less need for lipids, although some seeds do use oils as a food store. Carbohydrates and lipids can be made from glucose, because they contain the same chemical elements (carbon, hydrogen and oxygen). Proteins need nitrogen as well, but that is absorbed from the soil in the form of nitrates.

The main ways that glucose is used in plants after it is formed in leaves is shown in Figure 4.8.

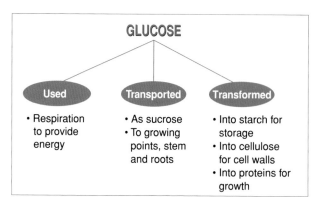

Figure 4.8 The fate of the glucose made in photosynthesis.

Why study respiration?

Every cell in every organ of every living organism on this planet needs energy. The energy is produced by the breakdown of food molecules, which store chemical energy. The process of respiration is how the food is broken down and the energy is released for use. If a cell stops respiring, it dies. Many other processes are needed for life, but respiration has to continue 24 hours a day, 7 days a week, for the whole of the organism's life.

Respiration occurs in every living cell. The usual food molecule respired is glucose (although it is possible to use others) and oxygen is used up in the process if respiration is **aerobic**, which it usually is. Carbon dioxide and water are produced as waste materials from the process. The word equation for aerobic respiration is:

glucose + oxygen $\rightarrow$ carbon dioxide + water + ENERGY

You may notice that this is the reverse of the equation for photosynthesis. Just like photosynthesis, aerobic respiration is a series of chemical reactions, each one controlled by a different enzyme.

PRACTICAL   HOW CAN WE MEASURE RESPIRATION?

This activity helps you with:
★ understanding aspects of experimental design
★ understanding control experiments.

Scientists can measure respiration in a number of ways.
• They can measure the uptake of oxygen (which is possible but difficult).
• They can measure the production of carbon dioxide (which is easy).
• They can measure the energy given off as heat during respiration. The useful energy produced in respiration is not heat, but chemical energy. However, whenever you get an energy change, some energy is lost as heat. The quantity of heat lost will be related to the amount of respiration occurring.

PRACTICAL *contd.*

Apparatus
* 2 × thermos flasks
* Mung beans, previously soaked in water
* 2 × thermometers
* Cotton wool
* Disinfectant

This experiment measures the heat given off by germinating seeds. In a germinating seed, there is rapid growth, so a lot of respiration goes on to provide the cells with the energy they need to grow.

Risk assessment

Your teacher will provide you with a risk assessment for this experiment.

Procedure
1 Set up the two thermos flasks as shown in Figure 4.9. Flask A is the experimental flask; flask B is a control, using boiled (dead) seeds.
2 Record the temperature of each flask.
3 Leave for 24 hours.
4 Record the temperatures again.
5 Record the results.

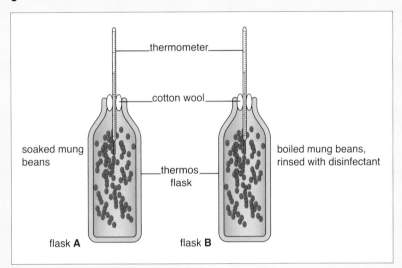

Figure 4.9 Experimental set-up.

Analysing your results
1 Explain your results for flask A.
2 Explain the purpose of flask B.
3 Why were the seeds in flask B rinsed in disinfectant? (Think what is likely to happen to dead seeds.)
4 Why were the seeds in flask A **not** rinsed in disinfectant?
5 Although there were roughly the same number of seeds in flask A and flask B, it is not necessary to have the same number (or the same mass) of beans in each flask. Why not?
6 Suggest a reason why it would not be a good idea to leave the seeds for much more than 24 hours before taking the second reading.

Cells do not always have a ready supply of oxygen. Some organisms live in places which are **anaerobic** (without oxygen) or where oxygen levels are very low. Even in humans and other mammals, oxygen levels in certain tissues can get very low (e.g. in muscle tissue during strenuous exercise). Yet, in either the short or long term, these cells survive.

They survive because they can respire **anaerobically**. Even without oxygen, certain cells can partially break down glucose and release some of the energy from it. Less energy is released than in aerobic respiration, but at least it's better than nothing.

In anaerobic respiration in **animals**, glucose is broken down into lactic acid, and the word equation is simple:

glucose → lactic acid + ENERGY

In **yeast** cells, anaerobic respiration results in different products:

glucose → ethanol + carbon dioxide + ENERGY

This reaction is used by humans, who brew alcoholic drinks by growing yeast in anaerobic conditions.

Figure 4.10 During a sprint, the athlete's muscle cells will not be able to get all the oxygen they need because of the huge demand for energy. The muscles respire anaerobically so that the sprinter's legs can keep moving.

PRACTICAL — HOW CAN WE MEASURE ANAEROBIC RESPIRATION IN YEAST?

Apparatus
* Culture of yeast cells in glucose solution
* Boiling tube
* Test tube
* Rubber bung
* Glass tubing
* Oil
* Stop watch

This experiment places a culture of yeast cells in anaerobic conditions and then measures the carbon dioxide given off as a measure of respiration. The glucose solution used is first boiled and cooled before adding the yeast cells, to remove any oxygen present. The yeast culture is then covered with a layer of oil to prevent any oxygen entering, so the conditions stay anaerobic.

Risk assessment

Your teacher will give you a risk assessment for this experiment.

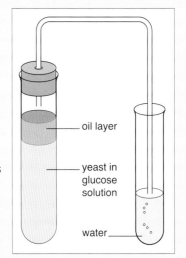

Figure 4.11 Apparatus set-up for measuring anaerobic respiration in yeast.

Procedure
1 Set up the apparatus as shown in Figure 4.11.
2 Leave it until there is regular bubbling from the end of the glass tubing.
3 Start the stop watch and count the number of bubbles given off per minute.
4 Repeat for 5 minutes.
5 Record your results.

Analysing your results
1 Counting bubbles per minute is not a very accurate way to measure carbon dioxide production (and therefore respiration). Why not?
2 How could the accuracy be improved?
3 From your results, do you think that five repeats were enough? Explain your answer.
4 Design an experiment to test the effect of temperature on anaerobic respiration in yeast. Ensure that the experiment is fair, and as accurate and repeatable as possible. Include a risk assessment.

PRACTICAL — WHAT EFFECTS DO RESPIRATION AND PHOTOSYNTHESIS HAVE ON THE ATMOSPHERE?

The processes of respiration and photosynthesis have opposite effects on the surrounding air. Photosynthesis adds oxygen and removes carbon dioxide, while respiration adds carbon dioxide and removes oxygen. The effects on carbon dioxide levels can be illustrated with a simple experiment involving aquatic organisms and bicarbonate indicator. Bicarbonate indicator can be used as a test for carbon dioxide, which is an acidic gas. The indicator detects small changes in acidity, as shown below:

ALKALI (carbon dioxide removed)	NEUTRAL	ACID (carbon dioxide added)
DEEP RED	ORANGE	YELLOW

continued...

Apparatus
* 5 × test tubes, labelled A–E
* Bicarbonate indicator
* Foil
* Cotton wool
* Test tube rack
* Pond weed
* Freshwater snails

(!) Risk assessment

There should be no risks associated with this experiment.

Procedure

1 Set up the five test tubes as shown in Figure 4.12.
2 Leave for at least 24 hours, in a brightly lit place.
3 Record the colour of the indicator in each tube.

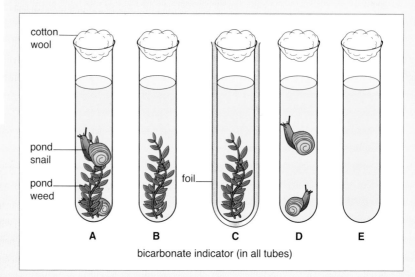

bicarbonate indicator (in all tubes)

Figure 4.12 Set-up of tubes A–E.

Analysing your results

1 Explain the final colour seen in each tube.
2 What was the purpose of:
   a tube C?
   b tube E?
3 Why were the tubes sealed with cotton wool rather than a cork or bung?

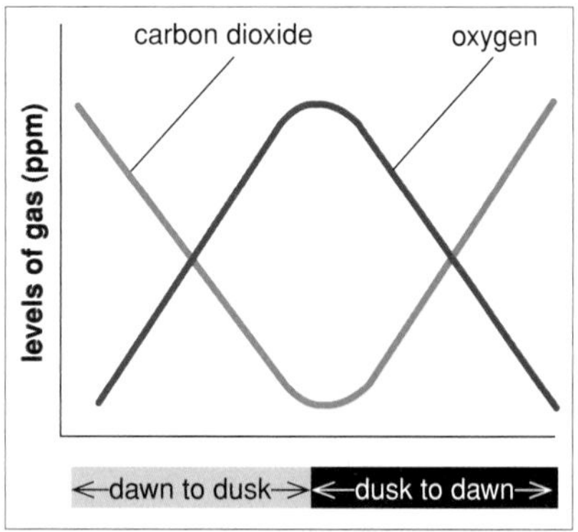

This experiment is **qualitative**. It does not *measure* anything. The indicator also only monitors the levels of carbon dioxide – we get no information about the levels of oxygen. To get a **quantitative** measure of oxygen and carbon dioxide, we would need to use electronic detectors attached to a data logger. Using this technology, the levels of carbon dioxide and oxygen were monitored in an enclosed area (a greenhouse) over 24 hours. The results are shown in Figure 4.13.

Figure 4.13 Levels of gases in a greenhouse in a 24-hour period.

QUESTIONS

1 Explain the trends shown in the graph (Figure 4.13).
2 The greenhouse contains very few animals. What changes would you expect to see in this graph if there was a mixed population of animals and plants?

Chapter summary

○ Plants need light, water and carbon dioxide for photosynthesis.

○ Plants need oxygen for respiration, although they usually make more than they need by photosynthesis.

○ Plants need minerals from their environment for certain purposes.

○ The light used for photosynthesis is absorbed by chlorophyll (in the chloroplasts of certain plant cells).

○ Temperature, and the levels of light and carbon dioxide, all affect the rate of photosynthesis.

○ The factor that is most important in limiting the rate of photosynthesis is called the limiting factor.

○ The chemical reactions in photosynthesis are controlled by enzymes.

○ The glucose made in photosynthesis can be converted into starch, cellulose and proteins.

○ Cells require a constant supply of energy to carry out life processes.

○ This energy is supplied by respiration.

○ During respiration, heat is released.

○ Aerobic respiration (when oxygen is present) involves the transformation of glucose and oxygen into carbon dioxide and water.

○ Respiration is a series of enzyme-controlled reactions.

○ In the absence of oxygen, anaerobic respiration may occur.

○ In animals, anaerobic respiration of glucose results in the formation of lactic acid.

○ In yeast, anaerobic respiration of glucose results in the formation of ethanol and carbon dioxide.

○ Anaerobic respiration produces less energy than aerobic respiration.

5 The respiratory system

We have seen in Chapter 4 that respiration is vital to all living things, and that it usually requires oxygen. This chapter looks at the system in mammals which provides the oxygen needed, getting it from the air and transferring it to the blood. This is the respiratory system.

What's the difference between respiration and breathing?

People sometimes get confused between respiration and breathing, thinking that they are two words for the same thing. They are not. The fact that the organs that we use to breathe are part of the respiratory system does not really help.

Respiration is the process that goes on in all living cells, releasing energy from food molecules (usually glucose) to provide for the cell's energy needs. In general, oxygen is needed for this.

Breathing is the way some animals get the oxygen they need for respiration. Plants don't breathe, and in fact many animals don't either. Many small animals can absorb oxygen through the surface of their body.

Why do we need a respiratory system?

As stated above, the function of the respiratory system is to extract oxygen from the air and get it into the blood, from where it can travel to all cells in the body. The respiratory system also removes carbon dioxide, which is a waste product of respiration. But why do we need a respiratory system when some animals manage without one? Animals without a respiratory system are all quite small. They absorb oxygen through their skin (or membrane, in the case of single celled animals). From the surface, the oxygen diffuses to all the cells in the animal. As these animals are small, there aren't many cells to supply with oxygen, and none of them are very far away from the surface. Diffusion is a slow process, but in such small animals it is fast enough, because of the small distance the oxygen has to travel. In larger animals, this will not work. If we absorbed oxygen through our skin, the cells deep inside our body would die before any oxygen had a chance to reach them.

All large animals therefore have a respiratory system of some sort, and these all have similar characteristics:

1 They have a very **large surface area** for their size. As oxygen enters through the surface of the respiratory organs, the more surface there is, the more oxygen can enter.
2 The respiratory surface is **thin**, so that it is easy for oxygen to diffuse through it.

3 The surface is **moist**, because oxygen needs to dissolve in order to get through into the blood. In the winter, you may have seen the result of this moisture, when you breathe out into cold air, and your breath appears as a sort of mist.

4 The respiratory organs are **well supplied with blood vessels**, because it is in the blood that the absorbed oxygen is carried away to the tissues.

What's in the respiratory system?

The respiratory system of a human is shown in Figure 5.1.

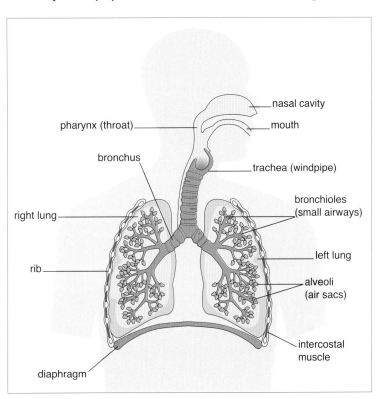

Figure 5.1 The human respiratory system.

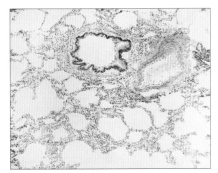

Figure 5.2 Microscope section of lung tissue: the lungs are sponge-like, and mostly composed of air.

Air travels into the body when we breathe in via the nose and mouth. It enters the lungs through the trachea, which splits into two bronchi (singular: bronchus), one going to each lung. Each bronchus splits into a number of smaller tubes, the bronchioles, which eventually end in an alveolus (plural: alveoli).

The respiratory system is protected by the ribs. The lungs are inflated and deflated using muscles – the intercostal muscles and the diaphragm (see 'How do we breathe?').

How do we breathe?

When the lungs expand, they suck air in; when they contract, they push air out again. There is no muscle in the lungs, though, so they cannot move on their own. The mechanism of breathing relies on the **diaphragm**, which is a sheet of muscle underneath the rib cage, and the rib cage itself, which is moved by the **intercostal muscles** between the ribs. It is also important to realise that the lungs are **elastic** (springy).

Breathing out is easiest to understand. When we breathe out, the intercostal muscles move the rib cage **downwards and inwards**, and the diaphragm moves **upwards**. This decreases the volume of the thorax and puts pressure on the lungs, so that the air in them is 'squeezed' out.

Breathing in is the reverse process. The rib cage is moved **upwards and outwards**, and the diaphragm **flattens**. This increases the volume of the thorax, and the lungs, because they are elastic, will naturally expand. The expansion of the lungs sucks air in through the trachea.

The breathing mechanism is summarised in Figure 5.3. Note that, during inspiration (breathing in), both the intercostal muscles and the diaphragm are contracted, and during expiration (breathing out) all the muscles are relaxed.

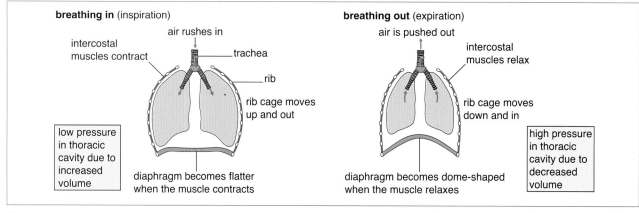

Figure 5.3 Mechanisms for breathing in and out.

This mechanism can be illustrated using an artificial model of the respiratory system, shown in Figure 5.4. The lungs are represented by the balloons, the rib cage by the bell jar, and the diaphragm by the rubber sheet. This is, in effect, two models in one. It is a model of the respiratory system as well as a model of the respiratory mechanism.

QUESTIONS

1 Explain why the balloons inflate when the sheet is pulled down, and deflate when it is pushed up.
2 List the ways in which this model of the respiratory system is inaccurate.
3 Do these inaccuracies mean that it is not a useful model of the respiratory *mechanism*? Explain your answer.

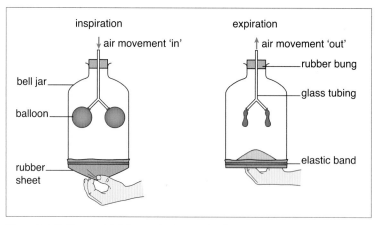

Figure 5.4 Bell jar model of the respiratory mechanism.

How is gas exchanged in the lungs?

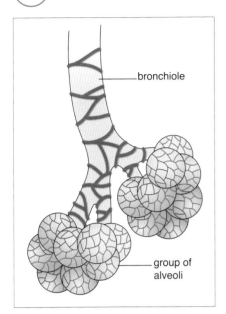

Figure 5.5 A cluster of alveoli at the end of a bronchiole. The millions of tiny alveoli give the lungs a huge area for gas exchange.

As you go deeper into the lungs, the tubes become narrower and thinner walled. The trachea and the bronchi, because they are relatively large in diameter, need support, which is provided by rings of cartilage. The smaller tubes, the bronchioles, are narrow and do not need this support. Each bronchiole ends in a group of thin walled sacs, or alveoli (singular: alveolus). It is in the alveoli, and only there, that gases are exchanged – oxygen goes out, into the blood, and carbon dioxide goes in.

Alveoli are ideal for gas exchange. They have a huge total surface area (the surface area of human lungs is roughly the size of a tennis court), they have very thin, moist walls and they are surrounded by blood capillaries.

Gas exchange occurs through the alveolus wall by diffusion. Oxygen diffuses from the air (where it is more concentrated) into the blood (where it is less concentrated). The blood carries the oxygen away from the alveolus, and the air content of the alveolus is refreshed with each breath, so that the concentration gradient is always maintained. For carbon dioxide, the situation is reversed, and it moves from the blood into the alveolus.

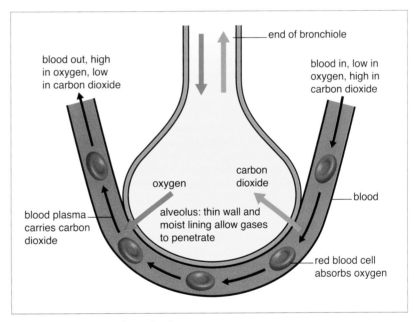

Figure 5.6 Gas exchange in an alveolus.

How does the air we breathe in differ from that we breathe out?

It is not true to say that we breathe in oxygen and we breathe out carbon dioxide. We breathe in air, and we breathe out air, but the composition of that air is different. This is summarised in Table 5.1.

Table 5.1 The composition of inhaled and exhaled air.

Gas	% in inhaled air	% in exhaled air
Oxygen	20.6	16.0
Carbon dioxide	0.04	4.0
Nitrogen	78.5	75.2
Water vapour	0.5	4.4
Other gases	0.4	0.4

In addition to the change in composition, the exhaled air is also warmer than the air we breathe in.

QUESTIONS

4 Why is the exhaled air warmer than the inhaled air?

5 Why does exhaled air have more water vapour?

6 Explain the change in the percentage of nitrogen in exhaled air (note: the body neither absorbs nor gives out nitrogen).

PRACTICAL

DEMONSTRATING THE DIFFERENCE IN CARBON DIOXIDE CONTENT OF INHALED AND EXHALED AIR

This activity helps you with:
★ drawing conclusions
★ designing valid experiments.

The apparatus shown in Figure 5.7 allows you to breathe in through one of the tubes (A) and out through the other (B). Lime water is placed in both tubes to test for carbon dioxide. Carbon dioxide turns lime water milky, but the test is not sensitive to small quantities of carbon dioxide.

 Risk assessment

There are no risks if the experiment is carried out correctly. Lime water (calcium hydroxide) is harmful if swallowed.

Procedure

1 Put the two pieces of rubber tubing in your mouth and breathe in and out gently through your mouth. When you breathe in, bubbles will be seen in tube A. When you breathe out, bubbles will be seen in tube B.

2 Continue to breathe in and out and observe the lime water to see when it goes cloudy.

Analysing your results

1 What are your conclusions from this experiment?

2 A student put forward a hypothesis that 'There is carbon dioxide in exhaled air but not in inhaled air'.

   a Explain why the evidence from this experiment cannot support this hypothesis.

   b Suggest how you could modify the procedure to test this hypothesis.

Discussion Point

Why does inhaled air come in through tube A and exhaled air go out through tube B?

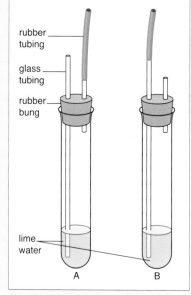

Figure 5.7 Apparatus to detect carbon dioxide in inhaled and exhaled air.

rubber tubing
glass tubing
rubber bung
lime water
A
B

How does smoking damage the lungs?

The worst thing you can do to your respiratory system is to smoke. When you smoke, you inhale a mixture of over 4,000 chemicals from the tobacco, and many of these are harmful. They include:

- 43 chemicals known to cause cancer (**carcinogens**).
- **Tar**, which is a sticky substance that clogs up the small air passages and alveoli in the lungs.
- **Nicotine**, which is a highly addictive substance.
- **Carbon monoxide**, a poisonous gas which makes it more difficult for the red blood cells to carry oxygen.
- A variety of other harmful substances including ammonia, formaldehyde, hydrogen cyanide and arsenic.

Smoking is linked to a wide variety of diseases, including many that are not connected with the respiratory system, like heart disease, stroke and cancers of the mouth, bladder, oesophagus, kidney, pancreas and cervix. Smoking is also a known cause of diseases of the respiratory system, such as:

- **Lung cancer:** 90% of lung cancers are thought to be caused by smoking. One in ten moderate smokers, and one in five heavy smokers die from the disease.
- **Emphysema:** The chemicals in tobacco smoke damage the walls of the alveoli, and eventually they break down. This means the alveolus can no longer be used to exchange gases, and the body suffers from low levels of oxygen. This causes breathing difficulties and can result in death.

Figure 5.8 Lung tissue damaged by emphysema. The dark spots are cavities, caused by the bursting of alveoli. Their colour is due to tar deposits.

As well as causing disease, the chemicals in the smoke also disable the respiratory system's defence mechanisms.

The trachea and bronchial tubes are lined with mucus, which keeps them moist and traps any particles, such as dust. In order to stop the mucus gradually sinking down into the lungs, the mucus is constantly moved upwards (to eventually be swallowed into the oesophagus) by small hair-like structures on the surface of the

Figure 5.9 Cilia on the surface of the cells lining the respiratory tubes.

cells lining the tubes. The structures are called **cilia**, and they are paralysed by the chemicals in cigarette smoke.

This paralysis means that harmful substances, including tar from the tobacco smoke, can now enter the smaller bronchioles and the alveoli. A further defence mechanism is coughing to try to 'blast' the irritants out of the lungs, and this is why smokers cough. Coughing, however, can also damage the alveoli.

The cilia remain paralysed for about 20 minutes, and if cigarettes are smoked this often over a long period of time, they remain paralysed, and eventually they will die off. They will then only regenerate if the smoker quits.

The evidence linking smoking and lung cancer

Evidence has been accumulated over the last 60 years about the links between smoking and lung cancer. It is well known that lung cancer is much more common in smokers, and that smokers can reduce their risk of lung cancer by giving up smoking (see Figure 5.10).

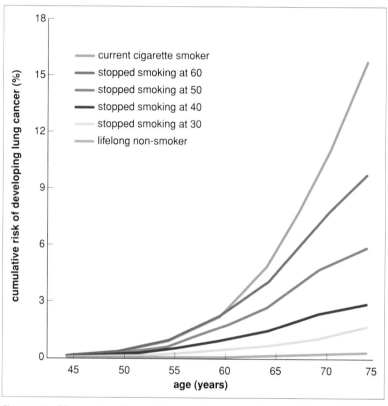

Figure 5.10 Effects of stopping smoking at various ages on the cumulative risk (%) of developing lung cancer by age 75 for men.

Discussion Point

Overall, smokers are about 15 times more likely to get lung cancer than non-smokers. In itself, however, this does not prove that smoking *causes* lung cancer. Why not, and what extra evidence is needed to show a causal link?

QUESTIONS

7 Compare the data of a lifelong non-smoker with someone giving up at 30. Roughly how much more likely is the smoker to develop lung cancer before the age of 65?

8 Suggest a reason why, if you smoke, it is best to give up before the age of 40.

WHAT'S IN CIGARETTE SMOKE?

This activity helps you with:
★ interpreting results
★ designing experiments.

This activity will be demonstrated in a fume cupboard by your teacher.

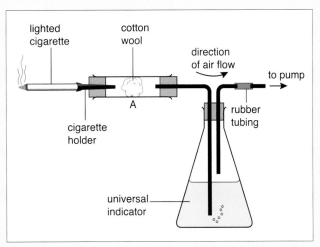

Figure 5.11 The 'cigarette machine'.

Air is sucked through the lighted cigarette. Observe the changes in the cotton wool and the universal indicator.

Questions

1 Suggest a reason for the colour change in the indicator.
2 Good practice in this experiment is to first suck air through an unlit cigarette for 10 minutes. Suggest a reason for this.
3 The colour and smell of the cotton wool shows the presence of tar. It is difficult to measure colour or smell. Suggest how the procedure could be adjusted so that the amount of tar in two different types of cigarettes could be compared.

How have attitudes to smoking changed?

Smoking was banned in all enclosed public spaces and work places in England, Wales and Northern Ireland in 2007. It had already been banned in Scotland in 2006. This was more than 50 years after the first scientific papers suggested a link between smoking and lung cancer. So, why did it take so long?

For quite a while, the evidence for smoking causing lung cancer was disputed, particularly by the tobacco industry. It stood to lose a lot of money if people stopped smoking, and could invest large sums in legal challenges and publicity.

Gradually, however, the scientific evidence accumulated, and this is a good example of how science works.

■ A great many studies found a clear link between smoking and the likelihood of getting lung cancer. These studies were published in scientific journals and were **peer reviewed** (checked by other scientists to make sure that the experimental technique was **valid** and that the evidence was of good quality).

- The large number of studies meant that there was good corroboration for the link (i.e. it wasn't just one study's conclusion, the evidence was confirmed over and over again).
- The sample of people tested and the length of the studies increased. One study, for instance, ran for over 40 years.
- There was a large difference between the incidence of lung cancer in smokers and non-smokers. This difference was clearly **significant**.
- More and more became known about the chemicals that were in tobacco smoke, and their effects. It is now known that the smoke contains 43 cancer-causing chemicals, so that as well as a link between smoking and cancer, there is also a **mechanism** that can explain *why* smoking causes cancer.
- People around a smoker also breathe in some smoke ('passive smoking'). There is increasing evidence that this raises their risk of getting cancer, too. The effects of this, and the level of increased risk, are still disputed by some people, although the scientific community generally accepts that passive smoking can be harmful to health (see the Task below).

TASK — WHAT ARE THE DANGERS OF PASSIVE SMOKING?

This activity helps you with:
★ judging validity of conclusions
★ assessing bias in sources.

This activity asks you to look at possible bias in the reporting of scientific research. Whilst it is logical that inhaling second-hand smoke, containing many harmful chemicals, is bad for health, the full extent of such dangers is not yet fully understood. You are asked to look at material on passive smoking produced by three groups, and see to what extent the reporting is biased. The three groups are:

- Cancer Research UK. This group can be considered to be unbiased.
- Forest. This is a UK pro-smoking group.
- ASH (Action on Smoking and Health). This group campaigns against smoking.

In the materials, look for examples of bias. Things to look out for are:

- **Selective reporting**. Evidence that goes against a group's point of view is simply ignored.
- **Selective quotes**. Picking individual statements supporting their point of view from a report, even when there are other comments which put a different point of view.
- **Exaggerating**, and then trashing, their opponent's claims.
- Selecting **individual examples** or **single studies** which validate the group's opinion, even when overall statistics or the majority of studies disagree.
- The evidence from any scientific experiment is never perfect. It is the duty of scientists to report both strengths and weaknesses in evidence. Biased groups may use statements of possible weakness in evidence to imply that the conclusions are invalid.

Look at the materials and write a report about their validity and bias. Cancer Research UK is part of the study as a sort of control. It can be assumed that the material they produce is accurate and reliable, as they have no vested interest. This does not mean that the material from the other two groups is definitely biased – that is for you to judge.

Chapter summary

- Most animals need a specialised respiratory system to absorb oxygen from the air into their blood, and to get rid of waste carbon dioxide from their blood into the air.
- The respiratory system consists of the nasal cavity, trachea, bronchi, bronchioles, alveoli, lungs, diaphragm, ribs and intercostal muscles.
- Inspiration occurs when the ribs move up and out and the diaphragm moves down, increasing the thoracic volume and decreasing pressure in the thorax. In expiration, these changes are reversed.
- Respiratory surfaces need to be thin and moist, and have a large surface area and a good blood supply.
- Gas exchange in mammals takes place in the alveoli, by diffusion.
- Inspired air has more oxygen, less carbon dioxide and less water vapour than expired air. It is also cooler than expired air.
- Dust and foreign bodies are prevented from entering the lungs because of the mucus lining and the cilia in the trachea and bronchi.
- Smoking paralyses and eventually destroys the cilia.
- Lung cancer and emphysema are two serious lung diseases that can be caused by smoking.
- Cigarette smoke contains carcinogens, tar and nicotine. All of these are harmful to the body.

Digestion

Why do we digest food?

We saw in the last chapter that animals get their energy from food. However, when we eat food it enters the gut, which is basically a tube that goes through the body. To be of any use, that food has to get out of the gut and into the blood system, which then can take it to any part of the body. There are two ways in which most of the food we eat needs to be changed so that it can get out of the gut and into the blood system.

1 The large molecules in the food have to be broken down into **small molecules**, which can be absorbed through the wall of the gut.
2 Insoluble molecules in the food have to be changed into water-soluble ones, so they can dissolve in the blood and be transported around.

The process of digestion makes these changes, breaking down complex food molecules into small, soluble ones. It is worth noting that some of the molecules we eat don't need digesting – they are already small and soluble (e.g. glucose and vitamins), but these are the exception rather than the rule.

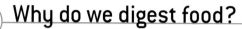

PRACTICAL   USING A 'MODEL GUT'

This activity helps you with:
★ designing experiments
★ interpreting results.

Visking tubing has similar properties to the lining of the gut and so we can use it as a 'model gut'. In this experiment, the water that the visking tubing is placed in represents the blood.

Risk assessment

Your teacher will give you a risk assessment for this experiment.

Apparatus
* Boiling tube
* Visking tubing, knotted at one end
* Elastic band
* 1% starch solution
* 1% glucose solution
* Iodine in potassium iodide solution
* 'Clinistix' glucose testing sticks

Procedure
1 Set up the apparatus as shown in Figure 6.1. Roughly half fill the visking tubing with starch solution and then top it up with glucose solution.
2 Leave for at least 30 minutes.
3 Remove the visking tubing but do not empty it.
4 Test the water in the test tube with a Clinistix stick to see if glucose is present*.
5 Add iodine solution to the water. A blue-black colour indicates starch; a brown colour means no starch is present.
6 Test the liquid from the visking tubing for starch and glucose.
7 Design a suitable table and record your results.

*As an alternative to using Clinistix, you could do a Benedict's test for sugar. This is described later in this chapter.

PRACTICAL *contd.*

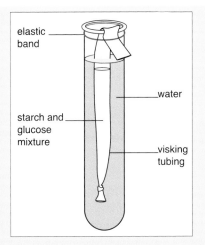

Figure 6.1 Experimental set-up.

Analysing your results

1 Explain what your results show about the gut and digestion.
2 Suggest why it is better to use a boiling tube in this experiment, rather than a beaker, which would hold more water.

Discussion Point

How good a model of the gut and blood system do you think this apparatus is? Justify your opinion.

What foods need digesting?

The complex food molecules in our diet fall into three categories:

1 Fats, which are broken down into glycerol and fatty acids.
2 Proteins, which are broken down into amino acids.
3 Some carbohydrates, the main one being starch, which is broken down in two stages, first to maltose, which is then converted to the simple sugar, glucose.

Not all these end products are used for energy. Energy is provided by glucose, glycerol and fatty acids, but the amino acids are not respired. Instead they are used as raw materials for making new proteins, which are needed for growth.

QUESTION

1 When people need energy very rapidly (e.g. athletes before strenuous exercise, diabetics with low blood sugar levels) they take glucose tablets or drinks. Why would glucose be a particularly good source of rapid energy?

This activity helps you with:
★ developing quantitative measurement techniques
★ judging the accuracy of measurement techniques.

There are chemical tests for a number of the different food groups: carbohydrates (with specific tests for starch and glucose), proteins and lipids.

Test for starch

When iodine solution is added to starch, the brown colour of the iodine turns to blue-black.

Test for glucose

When a solution containing glucose is heated with blue Benedict's solution, a reddish-orange precipitate is formed. As more and more precipitate is formed, the blue colour turns first to green, then orange, then to brick red. The more glucose there is, the more precipitate is formed. This test is called semi-quantitative, because it gives an idea (but not a precise measurement) of how much glucose is present.

Test for protein

A small quantity of dilute sodium hydroxide solution is added to the test solution, then a roughly equal quantity of copper sulfate solution is added. If protein is present, a purple colour is seen. This is called the **Biuret test**.

Test for lipids

A simple test for lipids is to rub the food to be tested on a sheet of paper. If it makes a translucent mark, the food contains lipid.

Investigating the Benedict's test for sugar

The full instructions for the Benedict's test are given below. It would be useful if you had done, or seen, the Benedict's test before attempting the questions that follow.

Risk assessment

Your teacher will provide you with a risk assessment.

Procedure

1 Place some test solution into the boiling tube. Make sure the tube is under half full.
2 Add enough Benedict's solution to give a distinct blue colour.
3 Half fill the beaker with water and bring it to the boil using the Bunsen burner.
4 Using the test tube holder, place the boiling tube in the beaker (see Figure 6.2).
5 Boil for 5 minutes, and observe the colour changes.

Questions

1 The more glucose there is in the solution, the further the colour change in the Benedict's solution goes. This gives an indication, but not a measure, of how much glucose is in the solution. Suggest how you might get an actual measure of the concentration of glucose in a solution, using the Benedict's test.
2 How accurate do you think your measure (from question 1) would be? Give reasons for your answer.

Apparatus

* 250 cm³ beaker
* Boiling tube
* Tripod
* Gauze
* Bunsen burner
* Test tube holder
* Heating mat
* Test solution
* Benedict's solution

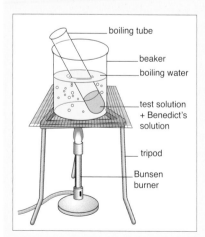

Figure 6.2 The Benedict's test.

boiling tube
beaker
boiling water
test solution + Benedict's solution
tripod
Bunsen burner

Where in the body is food digested?

Food is digested in the digestive system. This is basically a tube that goes through the body. The food is digested and the useful products are absorbed into the blood system as the food moves through the system, and eventually the non-digestible remains are 'egested', coming out the other end of the tube. The 'tube' is referred to as the gut, and different parts of it are specialised for specific functions.

Figure 6.3 shows you the digestive system and the functions of the various parts. As well as the gut, the digestive system also includes some associated organs (the liver, gall bladder and pancreas). There are three stages in digestion, which occur in different parts of the system.

1 **Digestion:** mainly in the mouth, stomach and small intestine.
2 **Absorption:** mainly in the small intestine (food) and large intestine (water).
3 **Egestion:** in the rectum and anus.

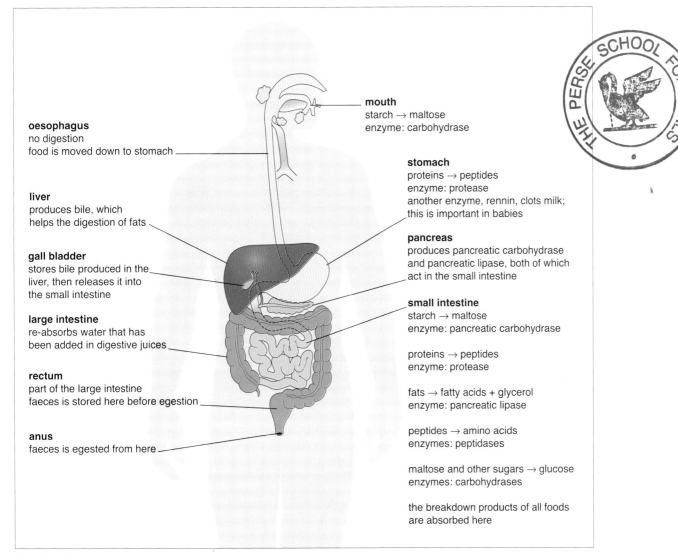

oesophagus
no digestion
food is moved down to stomach

liver
produces bile, which
helps the digestion of fats

gall bladder
stores bile produced in the
liver, then releases it into
the small intestine

large intestine
re-absorbs water that has
been added in digestive juices

rectum
part of the large intestine
faeces is stored here before egestion

anus
faeces is egested from here

mouth
starch → maltose
enzyme: carbohydrase

stomach
proteins → peptides
enzyme: protease
another enzyme, rennin, clots milk;
this is important in babies

pancreas
produces pancreatic carbohydrase
and pancreatic lipase, both of which
act in the small intestine

small intestine
starch → maltose
enzyme: pancreatic carbohydrase

proteins → peptides
enzyme: protease

fats → fatty acids + glycerol
enzyme: pancreatic lipase

peptides → amino acids
enzymes: peptidases

maltose and other sugars → glucose
enzymes: carbohydrases

the breakdown products of all foods
are absorbed here

Figure 6.3 The human digestive system.

Figure 6.4 summarises the digestion process, showing the stage by stage breakdown of each of the major food groups. By the time the food reaches the second half of the small intestine, digestion is complete and the breakdown products are all small, soluble molecules. These can then be absorbed into the blood. To help this, the walls of the small intestine are covered in small, finger-like projections called **villi**, which greatly increase the surface area over which food can be absorbed.

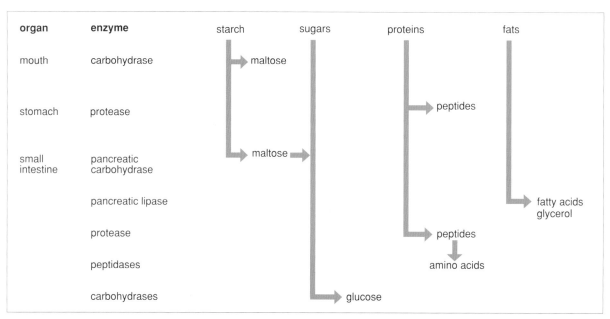

organ	enzyme	starch	sugars	proteins	fats

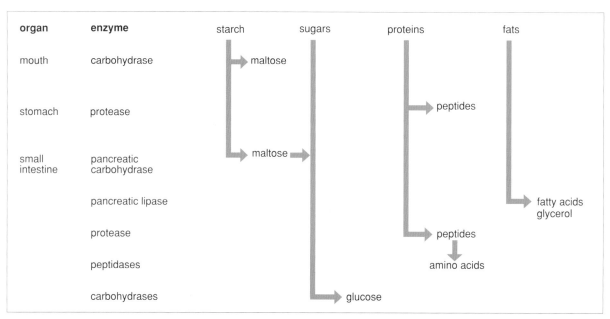

Figure 6.4 Summary of digestion.

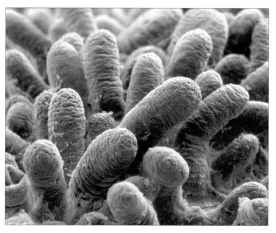

Figure 6.5 Surface of the small intestine, showing the villi.

QUESTION

2 As well as digesting proteins, the stomach also contains acid, which kills off bacteria present in the food. Why do you think this acid is best placed in the stomach rather than in
  a the small intestine or
  b the mouth?

By the time we reach the large intestine, all of the useful products have been absorbed into the blood. What remains is indigestible material, which will eventually be removed from the body as faeces. However, as it enters the large intestine, the material is a liquid, because of the digestive juices that have been added as it travelled down the gut. If this liquid was eliminated with the faeces, the body would soon dehydrate. The job of the large intestine is to re-absorb water from the waste, which will solidify as it goes down the large intestine. The now solid **faeces** are temporarily stored in the rectum before being egested via the anus.

DIGESTION

What does bile do?

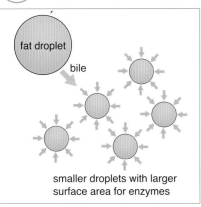

Figure 6.6 The effect of bile on fats.

Bile is produced by the liver and stored in the gall bladder. When a meal containing fat is being digested, the gall bladder releases bile down the **bile duct** into the small intestine. Bile is not an enzyme, but its job is to help the lipase enzyme in the small intestine to digest fats. Bile **emulsifies** fats, splitting the fat into small droplets, and allowing a greater surface area for the lipase enzyme to work (see Figure 6.6).

PRACTICAL — WHAT ARE THE OPTIMUM CONDITIONS FOR LIPASE ENZYMES?

In this experiment, liquid detergent is added to simulate the activity of bile. Like bile, detergent is an emulsifier. If available, bile salts could be substituted for the liquid detergent.

This activity helps you with:
★ interpreting results
★ evaluating experiments (for accuracy).

 Risk assessment

Your teacher will give you a risk assessment for this experiment.

Apparatus
* Full fat milk
* Phenolphthalein indicator
* 5% lipase solution
* Sodium carbonate solution, $0.05\ mol\ dm^{-3}$
* Liquid detergent
* Water baths set at 30 °C, 40 °C, 50 °C and 60 °C
* Ice
* Test tube rack
* $2 \times 10\ cm^3$ measuring cylinders
* $2 \times 100\ cm^3$ beakers
* $2 \times 250\ cm^3$ beakers
* 6 × thermometers
* 12 × test tubes
* Glass rod
* $2\ cm^3$ syringe
* Stop clock/stop watch

Procedure
Water baths will have to be set up in advance. Electronic water baths can be used for the temperatures above room temperature. Use the $250\ cm^3$ beakers to make water baths at 10 °C (cold water + ice) and 20 °C (tepid water). A beaker of lipase solution should be placed in the same or similar water baths, so that lipase is available at each of the test temperatures.

1. Add 5 drops of phenolphthalein indicator to two test tubes, for the first temperature.
2. Add $5\ cm^3$ of milk to each of the two test tubes.
3. Add $7\ cm^3$ of sodium carbonate solution to the test tubes, which should turn the phenolphthalein pink. The sodium carbonate is added to produce alkaline conditions, which is best for lipase.
4. Add 1 drop of liquid detergent to **one** of the test tubes.
5. Place both test tubes in the appropriate water bath. Test the temperature with the thermometer and leave until the contents of the tube have reached the experimental temperature.
6. Add $1\ cm^3$ of lipase to each tube and start the stop watch.
7. Stir the tubes gently, looking for the indicator to lose its pink colour.
8. Record the time taken for the colour change (in seconds).
9. Repeat for the other temperatures.
10. Record all your results in a table.
11. Plot a graph of temperature against time taken for the colour change. The graph should have two lines on it, one for the enzyme with liquid detergent and one without.

continued...

Analysing your results
1 What effect did temperature have on the enzyme activity?
2 What effect did the liquid detergent have on enzyme activity?
3 Looking at the results, do you think they were accurate? Give a reason for your answer.
4 Suggest one possible source of inaccuracy in this experiment.

Why does your tummy 'rumble'?

In order to move food along your digestive system, waves of muscle contraction constantly move along the gut. These waves are called **peristalsis**.

The circular muscles contracting just behind where the food is squeezes the food forward, rather like squeezing a toothpaste tube squirts the toothpaste out.

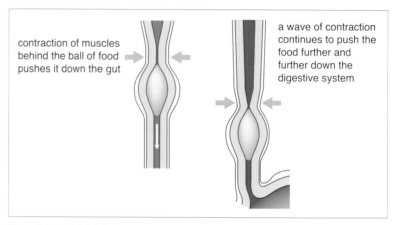

contraction of muscles behind the ball of food pushes it down the gut

a wave of contraction continues to push the food further and further down the digestive system

Figure 6.7 Peristalsis in the gut.

Peristalsis happens throughout the gut, including your stomach. When the stomach is full of food, the peristalsis simply moves the food around in the stomach, and this makes no noise. The stomach has rings of muscle at the entry and exit. When these contract, they close the openings at the top and bottom. When this happens, the food cannot move out of the stomach, and peristalsis simply churns it around, mixing it with digestive juices containing enzymes. If your stomach is empty, the only thing that can be squeezed by peristalsis is air inside the stomach. Moving air around the stomach creates a sort of gurgling or rumbling sound. We call this a 'rumbling stomach', and it is associated with an empty stomach, or hunger.

Chapter summary

○ Complex, insoluble food molecules need to be broken down into small, soluble molecules which can enter the blood system.

○ This breakdown, in the digestive system, is called digestion.

○ Digestion is aided by enzymes.

○ Enzymes work best at warm temperatures, but too high a temperature can destroy or 'denature' them.

○ Visking tubing behaves similarly to the wall of the gut, and it can be used as a 'model gut'.

○ Fats are digested into fatty acids and glycerol.

○ Proteins are digested into amino acids.

○ Starch is digested into glucose.

○ The test for starch uses iodine, which turns blue-black.

○ The test for glucose is the Benedict's test. The Benedict's solution (copper sulfate) is boiled and, if glucose is present, a reddish-orange precipitate is formed.

○ The test for protein is called the Biuret test. Copper sulfate and sodium hydroxide are added to the test solution. If protein is present, a purple colour appears.

○ The digestive system consists of the mouth, oesophagus, stomach, small intestine, large intestine, anus, liver, gall bladder and pancreas.

○ The mouth contains carbohydrase, which digests starch.

○ The stomach contains protease, which digests proteins.

○ The small intestine contains a variety of enzymes which complete the digestion of carbohydrates, proteins and fats.

○ The liver produces bile, which is stored in, and released from, the gall bladder.

○ Bile emulsifies fats, which aids their digestion.

○ Food is moved along the digestive system by peristalsis.

○ Glucose from carbohydrates, and fatty acids and glycerol from fats, provide energy for the body.

○ Amino acids from proteins form the building blocks for new proteins which are needed for growth and repair of tissues and organs.

Biodiversity and the environment

Environments are complex. They often contain a large number of different species which interact with each other in various ways. This chapter looks at the ways scientists tackle some of the problems of studying an environment.

What is biodiversity, and why is it important?

Biodiversity is the number of different species (of all types) in a particular area. It is not to do with the total numbers of animals and plants, but their variety. The 'area' concerned is of no fixed size – you could talk about the biodiversity on a sea shore, or in Wales, or in Europe, etc.

Biodiversity is a good thing, because it leads to stable environments that can resist possible harmful situations. Let's look at a type of environment which often has low biodiversity – a large field growing only one type of crop. Imagine that the crop is eaten by just one species of insect, and that the insect is eaten by just one species of bird. (No environment would ever be that simple, but it's just to show the principles in a simple way.)

In this environment, there is just one food chain (see Figure 7.1a).

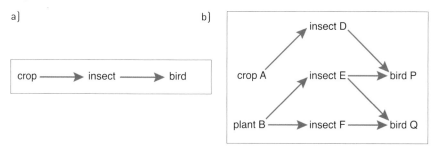

Figure 7.1 A food chain and a food web.

Now imagine that the farmer uses an insecticide to kill most of the insects. The birds will have nothing to eat and will go elsewhere, where they can get food. The few insects that survived will now not be eaten by anything, and their population will grow again very fast, causing severe damage to the crop, before eventually the birds will return, in response to the return of their food. A change in the population of one species can therefore have big effects on the others.

Now, let's consider a more complex environment with more organisms in it, and a **food web** (see Figure 7.1b).

Now suppose that the farmer kills many of insect species D with insecticide. This time, insect E, which does not feed on the crop, can supply food for bird P. Bird Q might now have less food to eat, but can still survive by eating insect F. All of the species can remain in the area, even if their numbers alter a bit. The environment is more **stable**.

In reality, there are always many more organisms in an environment than in these examples, but the principle holds true – the greater the biodiversity, the greater the stability of the environment.

Around the world, efforts are being made to preserve biodiversity, and to save endangered species. A lot of publicity is given to large animals, but biodiversity depends on keeping as large a variety of species as possible, and it is therefore important to conserve plants, worms, insects, spiders etc. as well (see Figure 7.2).

Biodiversity is also helpful in other ways. Hundreds of years of selective in-breeding in domestic and farm animals and crops have sometimes resulted in the loss of resistance to certain diseases. It is important we do not let the ancient breeds become extinct in case we need to strengthen current breeds, or re-introduce disease resistance, by cross-breeding them with ancient species in the future.

Figure 7.2 The fen raft spider, an endangered species found in the UK only in small populations in South Wales, Sussex and Suffolk. It is a semi-aquatic spider and efforts are being made to conserve its habitat so that its populations will grow.

Figure 7.3 The Soay sheep is an example of an ancient breed being conserved, whose genes may prove useful in the future.

How can biodiversity be maintained?

The first problem to be tackled if biodiversity is going to be maintained is to have a measure of it, and to repeat the measurement at intervals so that any changes can be identified. In the UK, a group called the UK Biodiversity Partnership collates data and assesses the biodiversity in the country by monitoring a set of 18 biodiversity indicators. Some data from the UK Biodiversity Partnership report for 2010 is shown in Figure 7.4.

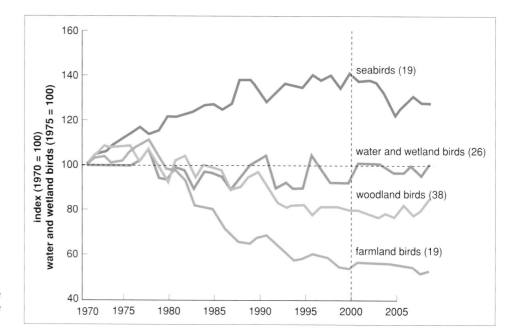

Figure 7.4 Changes in the populations of different types of birds in the UK, 1970–2008. The numbers in brackets indicate the number of species monitored.

Discussion Point

Suggest how the data in the graph might help to find reasons for the decline in woodland and farmland birds.

QUESTIONS

Over the study period seabirds have increased, water and wetland bird populations have been more or less stable, but there has been a decline in numbers of woodland and farmland birds.

1 Suggest a possible reason for the decline in woodland birds since 1970.
2 Suggest a possible reason for the decline in farmland birds since 1970.
3 The graphs go up to 2008. What do you think would happen to the populations of the different types of bird if further data had been published for 2010? Explain your answer.

Once accurate data for a population has been collected over a period of time, it is possible to use a mathematical model to predict what will happen to the population in the future, and to highlight possible future problems.

There are various ways in which biodiversity can be maintained, locally or nationally.

- Breeding and release programmes to boost populations.
- Active conservation of habitats of threatened species.
- Creation of habitats that have declined (planting, landscaping, etc.).
- Control of invasive species which may be spreading and pushing out other species.
- Legislation to protect habitats or individual species.
- Controlling pollution or other factors which might be threatening species or their habitat.

How can we get data about biodiversity in an environment?

Unless the environment studied is very small, the whole of it cannot be explored to find all the animals and plants living there. Plants are easier to find than animals, because they don't move around or hide, but even so, it would be impossible to count all the plants in, for example, a woodland with an area of several square kilometres. The only way we can get an idea of numbers is to take a **sample**. A small area is studied in detail, and the numbers used to predict the population numbers in the environment as a whole. For example, if we wanted to study a snail species in an area of marshland that is $100\,km^2$ in area, we might count all the snails in an area $100\,m \times 100\,m$ made up of many smaller samples. The whole sample area is $10\,000\,m^2$ which is $1/10\,000$ of the whole area. As an example, let us say there were 115 snails in the sample area, then

Sample area = 1/10 000 of total area

Number of snails in sample area = 115

Number of snails in total area = $115 \times 10\,000 = 1\,150\,000$

For this number to be reasonably accurate, certain criteria need to be met:

- The sample area must be typical of the whole area.
- Very small areas are more likely to be unusual in some way, and so the bigger the sample area is, the better.
- The method of sampling must not affect the results (e.g. with some animals, but not snails, the presence of humans might scare them away).

Samples cannot be absolutely accurate, and scientists often use statistical analysis which takes account of sample size when drawing conclusions.

QUESTIONS

4 Scientists sampled an area of $1000\,m^2$ on a beach that had an area of $1\,km^2$ ($1\,000\,000\,m^2$). They found 293 cockles. Estimate how many cockles there were on the whole beach.

5 Look at the environments in Figure 7.5. Suggest a reason why scientists would need to use a bigger sample area in woodland than in the saltmarsh.

Figure 7.5 Woodland (left) and saltmarsh (right) environments.

To sample a given area, scientists often use a piece of equipment called a quadrat. This is a frame of some sort with equal sides of a known length (see Figure 7.6).

The quadrat is used many times to build up a bigger sample area. It should be put down at random, to avoid the experimenter introducing any sort of bias into the data collection.

Figure 7.6 Using a quadrat. In this case, the quadrat is 0.5 m × 0.5 m, giving an area of 0.25 m².

PRACTICAL — COUNTING DAISIES

This activity helps you with:
★ designing experiments
★ developing mathematical skills.

Apparatus
* Quadrat, 0.5 m × 0.5 m
* Measuring tape

Risk assessment

Your teacher will provide a risk assessment for this experiment.

Procedure
1 Choose an area of grassland to sample, and measure the total area that you wish to study.
2 Place the quadrat 'randomly'. The easiest way to do this is to drop it over your shoulder, without looking where it will land. Always shout a warning to make sure no-one is behind you, or they may get hit with the quadrat.
3 Count the number of daisy *plants* (not just the flowers) in your quadrat.
4 Repeat another 9 times (i.e. 10 times in total).
5 Use your data to calculate how many daisies are in the whole area of grassland.

Evaluating your experiment
Suggest any possible disadvantages of the method used to place the quadrat randomly.

How can we find out about the distribution of organisms?

Sometimes, investigators don't want to just know what animals and plants are found in an environment, they also want to know something about their **distribution**. This can be done in a variety of ways, one of which is to do a **transect**. A transect is a series of samples taken in a line. The line chosen for the samples usually lies along some sort of changing conditions (e.g. when sampling a rocky shore, the transect might be lined up from the low tide level up to the high tide level – see Figure 7.7).

Figure 7.7 Students taking quadrat samples along a transect line laid up and down a rocky shore.

Quadrats are laid down at regular intervals along the transect line and the animals and plants in the quadrats are recorded. This allows any patterns of distribution to be detected (Figure 7.8).

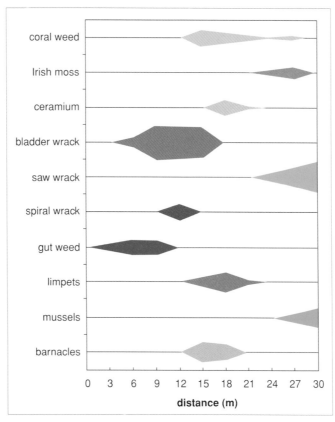

Figure 7.8 The distribution of organisms along a transect can be plotted as a 'kite diagram'. The width of the line is a measure of how many organisms of that type were found in quadrats placed at intervals along the transect.

WHAT EFFECT DOES TRAMPLING HAVE ON PLANTS?

This activity helps you with:
★ detecting patterns or trends in data
★ analysing results
★ identifying plant species.

For this experiment, you will need to find a path through your school grounds or any area of grassland or woodland. It is best to test a path that has been worn away by people walking along the route, rather than a constructed path, though this is not essential. Some plants can survive being regularly trodden on, and these will be found on or near the path. The less resistant a plant species is to trampling, the further away from the path it will be, until you reach a distance where people rarely tread.

Risk assessment

The experiment itself has no significant risks, but there may be risks associated with the environment. Your teacher will provide a risk assessment.

Apparatus

Per group:
* Quadrat, 0.5 m × 0.5 m
* 10 m string, marked every 0.5 m
* 2 × skewers or similar to anchor string into the ground
* Plant identification book

Procedure
1 Lay the marked string across the path, extending a roughly equal distance on either side. If the path is wide, lay the transect line on just one side of the path.
2 Lay the quadrat down every 0.5 m along the transect, and record the species found and the numbers of each. Do your best to identify all the plants that you find.
3 Present your results in any suitable way.

Figure 7.9 Suggested transect line to study plant distribution across a path.

Analysing your results
1 Is there any pattern in your results?
2 Of those plants found, which would you say is the most resistant to trampling? Justify your answer using your data.
3 Are there any other factors, apart from trampling, that might affect plant distribution in the area you sampled?
4 Is there any evidence of the influence of any other factor(s) in your results? Explain your answer.

How can we measure an animal population that moves around?

It is more difficult to measure animal populations in an area than plants, because animals move around. There is a danger of counting the same animal more than once, or of missing some which have just moved out of the sample area, but will return.

To determine the size of an animal population, **capture–recapture techniques** can be used. The technique works like this:

- A number of individuals of a particular species are captured.
- These animals are marked in some way so they can be distinguished from the rest of the population.
- They are then released back into the wild.
- Some time later, another sample of the species is captured.
- The proportion of marked individuals in the second sample would be the same as the number marked initially as a proportion of the total population.
- The population can be estimated using the equation $N = \dfrac{MC}{R}$ where:

  $N =$ estimate of total population size

  $M =$ total number of animals captured and marked on the first visit

  $C =$ total number of animals captured on the second visit

  $R =$ number of animals captured on the first visit that were then recaptured on the second visit

For the population estimate to be accurate, certain conditions must apply:

- Sufficient time has elapsed between the two samples for the marked individuals to mix with the rest of the population.
- There is no large scale movement of animals into or out of the area in the time between the two samples.
- The marking technique does not affect the survival chances of the animal (e.g. making it easier for a predator to see it).
- The marking technique does not affect the chances of recapture by making the marked individuals more 'noticeable' to the collector.

6 Dave wanted to estimate the population of woodlice in his garden. He searched around and collected 100 woodlice. He marked each of them with a spot of white paint on its back, and released them (see Figure 7.10). A week later he went into his garden and collected another 100 woodlice. Four of those were marked ones that he had captured before.

Using the equation given earlier in this section, calculate the size of the woodlouse population in Dave's garden.

Figure 7.10 Marked woodlouse.

Discussion Point

How good do you think Dave's experimental method was? Could he have improved it in any way?

Why can introducing new species to an area cause problems?

Although biodiversity is good, there can be problems if you introduce an 'alien' species (one not normally found in the area) into an environment. Examples of problems caused include:

- The alien species may have no predators in the area, and its population may grow out of control.
- The alien species may compete with an existing species, causing it to die out in the area.
- The alien species may prey on existing species, reducing their number.
- The alien species may carry a disease to which it has immunity, but the existing populations do not.

There are more than 3000 non-native species in the UK, more than in any other European country, so where have they all come from?

Some have arrived 'accidentally'. They may have arrived on board ships, amongst the cargo, or have been brought into the country by collectors or dealers and have then escaped or been released.

Figure 7.11 The fallow deer is not native to Britain. It was brought to this country by the Normans (or possibly the Romans), probably for hunting.

Some species are deliberately brought in to control pest species. This is an example of **biological control**. Biological control involves using living organisms (often predators) instead of chemical pesticides. They are often used to control other alien species, which may have no natural predators in their new environment.

In the early days of biological control, the process sometimes went wrong, and the introduced predator itself caused a problem. One example occurred in the United States, where exotic thistles had been accidentally introduced and were reducing the populations of the native thistles. A beetle, known to feed on the exotic thistles, was brought over in order to control them (Figure 7.12). However, when introduced into the area, the beetle also fed on native thistles. Certain local species of insect which fed only on the native thistles could no longer survive.

Figure 7.12 This beetle, *Rhinocyllusconicus*, was introduced into the USA to control alien species of thistle, but also ate the native thistles.

Scientists now understand the possible problems of introducing biological control agents and detailed research and extensive trials are now used before introducing any control species.

WHAT ARE THE ADVANTAGES AND DISADVANTAGES OF BIOLOGICAL CONTROL?

On the internet, research the pros and cons of biological control, and some of the different methods used. Write a report on your findings.

This activity helps you with:
★ developing research skills
★ selecting relevant information
★ organising ideas into a logical structure.

Chapter summary

○ Biodiversity is the variety or number of different species in an area.
○ Biodiversity increases the stability of the environment.
○ Assessing biodiversity requires the collection of reliable data and on-going monitoring.
○ Mathematical modelling can be used to analyse environmental interactions and predict trends.
○ When investigating an environment, samples have to be used when collecting data.
○ Samples must be large enough to represent the population as a whole.
○ Living things in an area can be investigated using quadrats and transects.
○ The capture/recapture technique can be used to estimate the size of animal populations.
○ Introducing alien species can have damaging effects on local wildlife.
○ Biological control agents have to be carefully studied before their introduction to avoid potential damage to local species.

Atomic structure and the Periodic Table

All chemical elements are made up of particles called **atoms**. You cannot understand chemical properties and reactions properly unless you know about the structure of atoms, and about the smaller particles that make up an atom.

What is the structure of an atom?

Every atom is made up of smaller particles called **protons**, **neutrons** and **electrons**. These are referred to as fundamental particles, and their numbers vary in atoms of different elements.

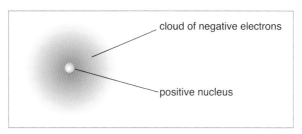

Figure 8.1 The structure of an atom.

The structure of an atom is shown in Figure 8.1. Every atom contains a positively charged central region called the **nucleus**. This is surrounded by light, negatively charged electrons. The positive and negative charges balance out so that the atom is electrically neutral.

The nucleus makes up nearly all the mass of the atom, and has two types of particle within it: protons, which have a positive charge, and neutrons, which have no charge. The collective name for protons and neutrons is **nucleons**. The mass of the positive proton is 0.00000000000000000000000017 g, which is very small. The mass of a neutron is the same as that of the proton. The mass of an electron is so small that it is considered to be negligible. For convenience, we can call the mass of a proton 1 unit and its charge +1, and describe the other particles relative to these values.

The properties of the different particles in an atom are summarised in Table 8.1.

Table 8.1 Relative masses and charges of fundamental particles.

Particle	Relative mass	Relative charge
Proton	1	+ 1
Neutron	1	0
Electron	Negligible	− 1

There are two other terms related to the structure of atoms which you need to know:

Atomic number: the number of protons in the nucleus. The number of electrons in an atom is always equal to the number of protons.

Mass number: the **total** number of nucleons (protons + neutrons) in the nucleus.

Sometimes, the chemical symbol for an element is written in a way that shows the atomic number and the mass number. An example is given on the left, for the element sodium.

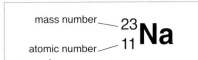

mass number $\longrightarrow$ ^{23}**Na**
atomic number $\longrightarrow$ $_{11}$

Figure 8.2 Chemical symbol for sodium.

QUESTION

1 Look at the information about the sodium atom. How many protons, neutrons and electrons are there in the atom?

The electrons in an atom are at different **energy levels** around the nucleus. The energy levels are sometimes called **shells** or **orbits**. Each shell can contain only a certain number of electrons as shown in Table 8.2.

Table 8.2 The number of electrons held by different shells

Shell (or orbit)	Maximum number of electrons accommodated for elements hydrogen to calcium
1	2
2	8
3	8
4	2

Example

The element sodium, Na, has an atomic number of 11. This means that it has 11 protons in the nucleus, and so must have 11 electrons surrounding the nucleus. These 11 electrons are arranged as shown in Table 8.3.

Table 8.3 Arrangement of electrons in the sodium atom.

Shell (or orbit)	Number of electrons
1	2
2	8
3	1
	11 electrons in all

The electronic structure for sodium can be written as 2,8,1 and it can be depicted as in Figure 8.3.

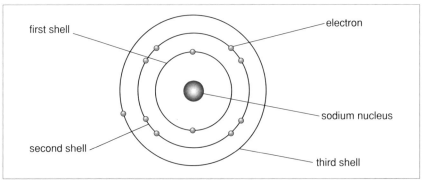

Figure 8.3 Electronic structure of a sodium atom.

Table 8.4 shows the electronic structure for the first 20 elements in the Periodic Table. Note that each time the atomic number goes up, this means there is an extra proton. As the number of electrons always equals the number of protons, an extra electron is also added. This goes into the next available position in a shell or, if the shell is full, into the first position of a new shell.

Table 8.4 Electronic structures of the first 20 elements of the Periodic Table.

| Atomic number | Element | Shell | | | |
		1	2	3	4
1	Hydrogen	1			
2	Helium	2			
3	Lithium	2	1		
4	Beryllium	2	2		
5	Boron	2	3		
6	Carbon	2	4		
7	Nitrogen	2	5		
8	Oxygen	2	6		
9	Fluorine	2	7		
10	Neon	2	8		
11	Sodium	2	8	1	
12	Magnesium	2	8	2	
13	Aluminium	2	8	3	
14	Silicon	2	8	4	
15	Phosphorus	2	8	5	
16	Sulfur	2	8	6	
17	Chlorine	2	8	7	
18	Argon	2	8	8	
19	Potassium	2	8	8	1
20	Calcium	2	8	8	2

QUESTIONS

2 Using the information in Table 8.4, draw the atoms of:

a carbon

b hydrogen

c silicon

d potassium.

3 Which element's atom is shown in this diagram (Figure 8.4)?

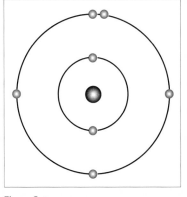

Figure 8.4

In the GCSE Science course, you learnt about the **Periodic Table of the elements**. The electronic structure of an element is related to its position in the Periodic Table. The table arranges the elements in order of their atomic number. As the atomic number is the number of protons, it also represents the number of electrons.

Look at the Periodic Table (Figure 8.5) and the electronic structures shown in Table 8.4.

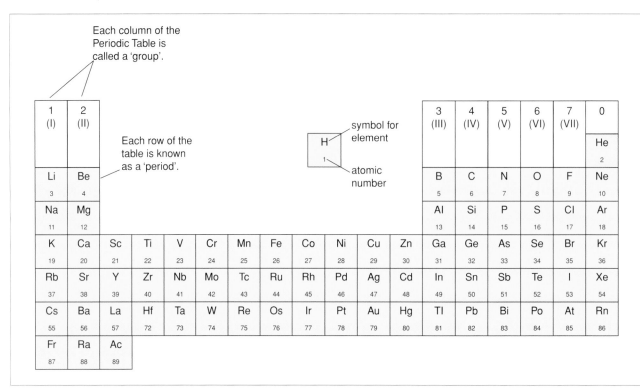

Figure 8.5 The modern Periodic Table.

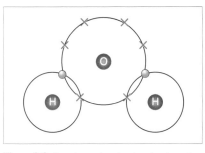

Figure 8.6 A water molecule, showing how the hydrogen and oxygen atoms 'share' electrons.

QUESTIONS

4 Look at the first 20 elements, and which group they are in. What is the connection between the group number and the electronic structure? (Note: hydrogen is not in a group.)

5 For the first 20 elements, what is the relationship between the **period** the element is in and its electronic structure?

You will see later that the electronic structure of an element affects its chemical properties, because, for example, elements can share electrons when forming compounds (see Figure 8.6).

What is an isotope?

Figure 8.7 The common isotope of oxygen (left), and the 'oxygen 17' isotope (right).

Different elements have different atomic (proton) numbers, and no two elements have the same number of protons. However, the number of neutrons in the nucleus is not fixed. Some atoms of the same element have different numbers of neutrons and so they have different mass (nucleon) numbers. These different forms of the same element are called **isotopes**.

Two isotopes of oxygen are shown in Figure 8.7. You will see that both isotopes have the same atomic number, because they both have eight protons (otherwise, the atom would not be an oxygen atom at all). However, their mass numbers are different, because ^{16}O has eight neutrons and ^{17}O has nine.

When isotopes have more neutrons than protons, the atom is sometimes unstable and likely to decay. Such isotopes are radioactive. The more the number of neutrons differs from the stable form, the more likely it is that the atom will be radioactive. For example, the common form of carbon, ^{12}C, has six neutrons and six protons. The isotope ^{13}C has one extra neutron but is stable, whereas ^{14}C is unstable and radioactive.

TASK — HOW CAN ISOTOPES BE DANGEROUS?

This activity helps you with:
★ researching information
★ developing communication skills
★ understanding more about isotopes.

Research isotopes and explain how some can be deadly. You may want to refer to the case of Alexander Litvinenko, a former Russian security officer who died in 2006 under mysterious circumstances. It was thought that his death was caused by a radioisotope.

How heavy is an atom?

If you try to express the weight of an atom in grams, the number would be incredibly small. To have figures that are easier to use, scientists express the mass of an atom relative to the weight of the carbon atom, ^{12}C. The mass of ^{12}C is given as 12, its mass number, and the masses of other atoms are then calculated from that. These figures are called **relative atomic masses**, and given the symbol A_r.

The relative atomic masses of some common elements are given in Table 8.5.

Table 8.5 A_r values for some common elements.

Element	A_r	Element	A_r
H	1.0	P	31.0
He	4.0	S	32.0
C	12.0	Cl	35.5
N	14.0	K	39.0
O	16.0	Ca	40.0
F	19.0	Fe	56.0
Na	23.0	Cu	64.0
Mg	24.0	Ag	107.0
Al	27.0	Pb	207.0

The word *relative* is important here. In Table 8.5, the relative atomic mass of magnesium is given as 24. That means that it is twice the mass of a carbon atom – it is not really a measurement of mass, and so A_r has no units.

If we know the relative atomic masses of the elements, then we can work out the **relative molecular masses** (M_r) of compounds:

■ **Water** (H_2O): In this molecule, there are two hydrogen atoms and one oxygen atom. The relative molecular mass is $[(2 \times 1) + 16] = 18$.
■ **Carbon dioxide** (CO_2): In this molecule, there are two oxygen atoms and one carbon atom. The relative molecular mass is $[(2 \times 16) + 12] = 44$.

For ionic compounds, it is more correct to use the term **relative formula mass**, as there are no separate molecules in ionic compounds.

■ **Magnesium oxide** (MgO): In this compound, there is one magnesium ion for every one oxygen ion. The relative formula mass equals [24 + 16] = 40.
■ **Sodium carbonate** (Na_2CO_3): In this compound, there are two sodium ions, and one carbonate ion made up of one carbon and three oxygen atoms. The relative formula mass equals [(2 × 23) + 12 + (3 × 16)] = [46 + 12 + 48] = 106.

QUESTIONS

6 Find the relative molecular masses of:
   a ammonia, NH_3
   b methane, CH_4
   c hydrogen sulfide, H_2S
7 Find the relative formula masses of:
   a calcium chloride, $CaCl_2$
   b copper(II) oxide, CuO

How has the model of atomic structure been developed?

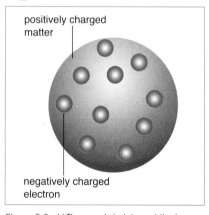

Figure 8.8 JJ Thomson's 'raisin pudding' model of an atom.

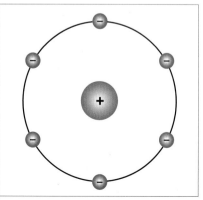

Figure 8.9 Rutherford's first model of the atom.

Atoms are too small to be seen. Therefore, all ideas about their structure are **scientific models**, based on evidence of various sorts. Over time, new evidence has meant that scientists have had to revise the model, because the new evidence could not be explained by the existing one.

The term atom was first used by the Greek philosopher Democritus about 460 BC. He did not suggest a structure, however, merely that, if you continued breaking pieces of matter apart, eventually you would come to something you could not break down any further, which he called an atom.

The first suggested structure of an atom was by the English physicist JJ Thomson in 1897. He discovered electrons and found that they had a negative charge. He imagined that they must be embedded in positively charged matter, rather like raisins in a pudding (Figure 8.8).

In 1911, research by the scientist Ernest Rutherford produced results that this model could not explain. Rutherford bombarded atoms with alpha radiation particles, and found that most of the particles went through the atoms without being deflected. This indicated that most of the atom must be empty space. He suggested a model of the atom that consisted of a tiny positively charged nucleus surrounded by orbiting electrons, but he knew nothing at this stage about protons and neutrons (Figure 8.9).

Various modifications were made to this model over a number of years, and these are detailed on the next page.

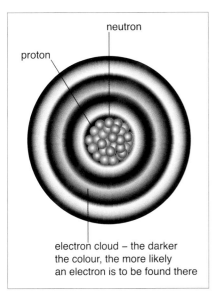

proton

neutron

electron cloud – the darker the colour, the more likely an electron is to be found there

Figure 8.10 Modern model of an atom.

1912 Danish physicist Niels Bohr came up with a theory as to why electrons do not spiral into the nucleus due to its positive charge; he proposed that electrons circulate in distinct orbits (shells)

1919 Rutherford discovered protons

1927 German scientist Werner Heisenberg suggested that the exact position of an electron cannot be determined. This is why the modern model depicts as an 'electron cloud' rather than a distinct orbit

1932 Neutrons discovered by English physicist James Chadwick

Research about atoms and particles has progressed considerably since 1932, but the sorts of models now used are mathematical models, and these cannot really be shown in pictures. There are now known to be many different types of particles beyond just protons, neutrons and electrons. In fact, there are around 50 types, some of them having strange names like 'Charm', 'Anti-charm', 'Gluon', 'Up' and even 'Strange'!

The changes in the model of atomic structure indicate a fundamental principle of science. No scientific model can ever be said to be absolutely correct. If our model of atomic structure was absolutely correct, it would no longer be a model, it would *be* the structure of an atom. Models have to be continuously changed and improved as a result of new research. Although there are undisputed facts in science, most of science deals with probabilities and uncertainty.

Chapter summary

- ◯ Atoms have a nucleus consisting of protons and neutrons, surrounded by electrons.
- ◯ Protons have a positive charge, electrons a negative charge, and neutrons have no charge.
- ◯ There is always an equal number of protons and electrons in an atom, which therefore has no electrical charge.
- ◯ The number of neutrons in an atom can vary, producing different isotopes of the element.
- ◯ Protons and neutrons are equal in mass, but the mass of electrons is negligible.
- ◯ The number of protons gives the element's atomic number.
- ◯ The number of nucleons (protons + neutrons) gives the element's mass number.
- ◯ A symbol such as $^{23}_{11}$Na can be used to calculate the number of protons, neutrons and electrons in an atom.
- ◯ The electronic structure of an atom is related to its position in the Periodic Table and its chemical properties.
- ◯ The mass of an atom of an element is measured on a scale which compares masses of atoms with each other – relative atomic masses (A_r).
- ◯ The relative molecular mass (M_r) of a compound can be calculated from its formula.
- ◯ The accepted model of an atom has developed over time as scientists made observations that could not be explained by contemporary ideas, and therefore proposed their own hypotheses to be tested by gathering further experimental evidence.

9 Alkali metals and halogens

One of the most spectacular reactions in school chemistry is potassium reacting with water (Figure 9.1). Few demonstrations can match this reaction for sheer brilliance. Potassium is one of the family of metals called the **alkali metals** which occupy Group 1 of the Periodic Table (see Figure 9.2).

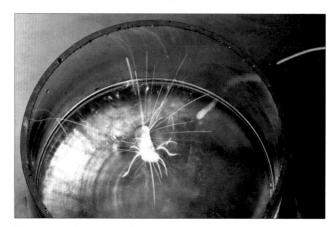

Figure 9.1 Potassium reacting with water.

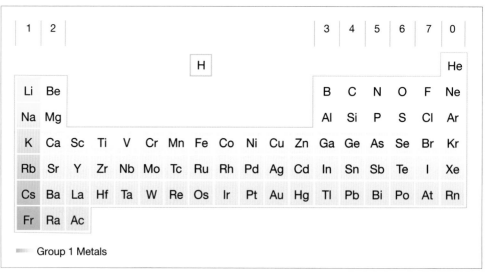

Figure 9.2 Periodic Table highlighting Group 1.

Another spectacular reaction is the combustion of sodium in chlorine gas (Figure 9.3).

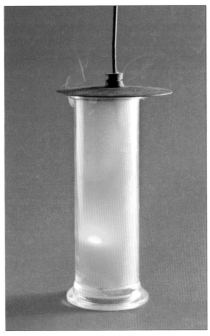

Figure 9.3 Sodium burning in chlorine.

Chlorine is a member of Group 7 of the Periodic Table called the **halogens** ('salt formers with metals').

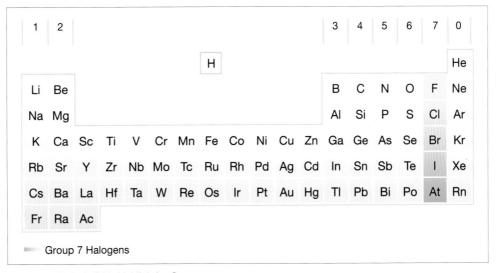

Figure 9.4 Periodic Table highlighting Group 7.

The alkali metals

There are six elements in Group 1 of the Periodic Table; these are the alkali metals (so called because when they react with water they form hydroxides which are alkaline solutions). Some information about the alkali metals is given in Table 9.1.

Table 9.1   Alkali metals.

Alkali metal	Symbol (mass number / symbol / atomic number)	Electron structure	Appearance
Lithium	$^{7}_{3}Li$	2,1	
Sodium	$^{23}_{11}Na$	2,8,1	
Potassium	$^{39}_{19}K$	2,8,8,1	
Rubidium	$^{85}_{37}Rb$	2,8, … ,8,1	
Caesium	$^{133}_{55}Cs$	2,8, … , … ,8,1	
Francium	$^{223}_{87}Fr$	2,8, … , … , … ,8,1	

Being in the same group of the Periodic Table, they all react with other chemicals in very similar ways.

Alkali metal reactions

With oxygen in air

All the alkali metals are **soft shiny metals** that react on contact with air (in fact they are all so reactive with air that they are stored in bottles of clear oil).

Figure 9.5 shows lithium a) stored under oil and b) on contact with air.

Figure 9.5 a) Lithium stored under oil (shiny silver colour).

b) Lithium in contact with air (dark grey lithium oxide coating).

As soon as the bare lithium comes into contact with oxygen in the air it reacts, forming lithium oxide, Li_2O.

lithium + oxygen $\rightarrow$ lithium oxide

$$4Li(s) + O_2(g) \quad \rightarrow \quad 2Li_2O(s)$$

(The letters in brackets tell you the state of the reactants and products: s = solid; g = gas.)

The other metals in the group react in similar ways (see the Practical beginning on page 87).

With water

The alkali metals all react vigorously with water. Lithium fizzes in contact with water, forming the alkali lithium hydroxide and bubbles of hydrogen gas.

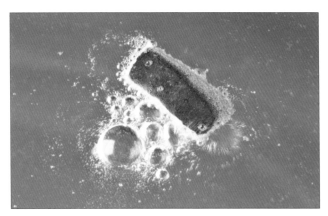

Figure 9.6 Lithium reacting with water.

lithium + water $\rightarrow$ lithium hydroxide + hydrogen

$$2Li(s) + 2H_2O(l) \rightarrow \quad 2LiOH(aq) + H_2(g)$$

The other metals in the group also react in similar ways.

With chlorine (and bromine)

Lithium reacts strongly with chlorine, producing the salt lithium chloride, LiCl.

Figure 9.7 Lithium burning in chlorine.

lithium + chlorine → lithium chloride

$$2Li(s) + Cl_2(g) \rightarrow 2LiCl(s)$$

Lithium reacts with bromine in a similar way, forming lithium bromide:

lithium + bromine → lithium bromide

$$2Li(s) + Br_2(g) \rightarrow 2LiBr(s)$$

The other alkali metals have similar patterns of reactivity with the halogens as they have with oxygen and water.

PRACTICAL OBSERVING PATTERNS OF REACTIVITY – THE ALKALI METALS

The alkali metals all react vigorously with oxygen (in air), water and chlorine. In this task you will observe the reactions of three of the alkali metals, lithium, sodium and potassium, with these reactants, record your observations and analyse them in terms of a metal reactivity series. **Your teacher will demonstrate each of these reactions.**

This activity helps you with:
★ observing reactions of alkali metals
★ recording observational details about reactions
★ examining patterns of reactivity to determine a reactivity series
★ writing balanced chemical symbol equations.

 Risk assessment

All the reactions involving alkali metals are so vigorous that they must be performed by demonstration only in schools. Your teacher will give you a suitable risk assessment for these reactions.
DO NOT ATTEMPT TO BURN POTASSIUM IN AIR.
DO NOT ATTEMPT TO BURN POTASSIUM IN CHLORINE.

Procedure

You will need to copy and complete a version of Table 9.2 to record your observations.

Table 9.2 Results table.

Reaction with	Lithium	Sodium	Potassium
Oxygen (in air) Tarnishing			
Oxygen (in air) Burning			
Water			
Chlorine			

Apparatus for demonstration
* lithium, sodium and potassium metals stored under oil
* cutting tile
* forceps
* scalpel
* brick
* Bunsen burner
* (optional) demonstration camera/digitiser/view-flexi-cam connected to computer/projector

Reaction with oxygen in air
1 Your teacher will remove a piece of lithium from its storage jar using forceps.
2 The lithium is placed on a white cutting tile and cut in half with a scalpel.
3 Observe and record the reaction that occurs between the oxygen in the air and the cut surface of the lithium.
4 A piece of lithium is placed on the flat surface of the brick. Your teacher will return any unused cut pieces of lithium to their jar.
5 Your teacher will direct a non-luminous Bunsen burner flame onto the lithium so that it melts, any oil burns off and then it ignites.
6 Observe and record the combustion reaction of lithium with oxygen (in air).
7 Repeat the **tarnishing** experiments for sodium and potassium, and the combustion experiment for sodium (NOT POTASSIUM).

continued...

Apparatus for demonstration
As above plus:
* water trough
* safety screen
* boiling tube
* universal indicator (UI)
  paper/solution

Apparatus for demonstration
As for reaction with air plus:
* x2 inverted gas jars filled
  with chlorine (produced by
  method on CLEAPSS Hazcard
  89A)
* small flat-surfaced brick
  larger than diameter of gas
  jar
* Bunsen burner
* tissue paper
* safety screen

Reaction with water

1 Your teacher will remove a piece of lithium from its storage jar using forceps.
2 The lithium is placed on a white cutting tile and cut in half with a scalpel.
3 The lithium is dropped into a water trough behind a safety screen.
4 Observe and record the reaction that occurs between the water and the lithium.
5 Your teacher will dip a piece of UI paper into the water near to where the lithium was reacting. Observe and record the colour change of the UI paper.
6 Repeat with sodium and potassium.
7 When all the reactions have been completed, your teacher will transfer a small amount of the water into a boiling tube and add a few drops of UI solution; observe and record any colour changes.

Reaction of lithium and sodium with chlorine

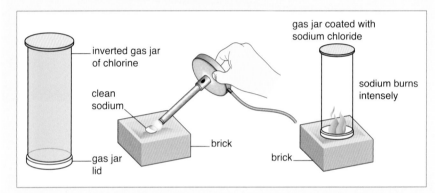

Figure 9.8 Experimental set-up.

1 Your teacher will cut a piece of lithium (a 6–8 mm cube is sufficient) and remove the oil by squeezing the cube between tissue paper.
2 The lithium is placed on the flat side of a brick in a fume cupboard.
3 Your teacher will direct a non-luminous Bunsen burner flame onto the lithium so that it melts and any remaining oil burns off.
4 When the lithium finally starts to burn with a small red flame, your teacher will quickly remove the lid of the gas jar of chlorine and place the gas jar over the burning lithium.
5 Observe and record the reaction that occurs.
6 Repeat with sodium.

DO NOT REPEAT THIS EXPERIMENT WITH POTASSIUM.

Analysing your results
The following questions are based on your observations of the reactions of the alkali metals with oxygen (in air), water and chlorine.

1 Which alkali metal reacts most vigorously with:
  a air?
  b water?
  c chlorine?
2 Using your observations, arrange the three alkali metals in order of their reactivity (from least reactive to most reactive).
3 Using a Periodic Table, arrange **all** the Group 1 metals in order of reactivity.

4 How does reactivity vary as you move down Group 1 of the Periodic Table?

5 Look again at the electronic structure of the alkali metals in Table 9.1. Is there a pattern between the electron structure and the reactivity of the alkali metals? Can you explain the pattern?

6 Predict the observations that you might make from the reactions of rubidium with oxygen (in air), water and chlorine.

7 Why are the reactions of potassium with chlorine, and any of the other alkali metals with any of the other chemicals, **not** allowed to be carried out in schools?

8 Use the word and balanced symbol equations for lithium to produce similar word and balanced symbol equations for the reactions of sodium and potassium with oxygen, water and chlorine.

9 Bromine is a halogen like chlorine but it is **less** reactive than chlorine gas. Predict the reactions of bromine with lithium, sodium and potassium.

10 Write word and balanced symbol equations for the reactions of bromine with lithium, sodium and potassium.

> **Discussion Point**
>
> Rubidium and caesium react far too violently with oxygen, water and chlorine to be performed even by demonstration in schools. You can, however, see video clips online of these reactions occurring under very special controlled conditions. The best example of this is Brainiac: Science Abuse! www.youtube.com/watch?v=m55kgyApYrY

Flame tests

You will have noticed that the three alkali metals that you have seen tested burn in oxygen (in air) with different coloured flames. Lithium burns with a crimson-red colour, sodium with an orange-yellow flame, and potassium with a lilac-purple colour.

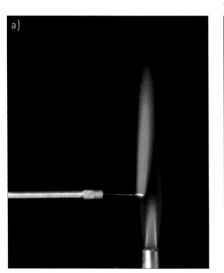
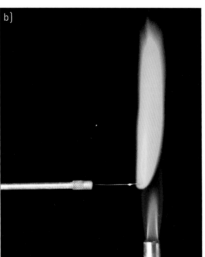

Figure 9.9 Colours of a) lithium b) sodium and c) potassium flames.

It turns out that even when these metals are combined with other elements to form salts such as lithium nitrate, sodium chloride or potassium sulfate, these salts also burn with the same colour of flame as the metal ion in them. This means that all lithium salts burn with a crimson red colour, sodium salts burn with an orange-yellow colour and potassium salts burn with a lilac-purple colour.

This activity helps you with:
★ performing a flame test
★ designing a suitable table to record experimental observations
★ observing and recording alkali metal reactions
★ comparing three experimental techniques
★ (optional) producing a risk assessment.

There are three easy methods for performing a flame test of an alkali metal salt:

- Sprinkling alkali salt powder into a roaring Bunsen flame from above.
- Spraying alkali metal salt solution into a roaring Bunsen flame from the side.
- Sticking alkali metal salt powder on to a flame test probe after washing with 2 M hydrochloric acid and then placing the flame test probe into a roaring Bunsen flame.

You will perform each technique on a range of different alkali metal salts; observe and record your findings; and then use your results to compare each flame test technique.

 Risk assessment

Your teacher may ask you to produce a risk assessment for this activity. You will be provided with a suitable blank risk assessment form and the relevant Hazcards, Student Safety Cards or CLEAPSS guidance in order for you to complete the risk assessment. You must show your teacher your completed risk assessment before attempting the practical activities.

Alternatively, your teacher will provide you with a suitable risk assessment.

Wear goggles throughout this practical.

Procedure

Your teacher will tell you which alkali metal salts are available for you to use. You need to design a suitable table to record the colour of the flames for each alkali metal salt by each flame test technique.

We suggest that you do all the tests for lithium and potassium salts before attempting any of the sodium salts – the sodium flame tends to dominate any other flame, even with very small quantities of sodium salt.

Sprinkle method
1 Ensure your Bunsen burner is sitting on a heatproof mat.
2 Using a spatula, sprinkle a small amount of alkali metal salt into a roaring Bunsen burner flame from at least 30 cm above the flame.
3 Observe the reaction and record your observations. (Use this method with the lithium and potassium salts first.)
4 Observe the potassium flame through a cobalt-blue filter if the yellow sodium flame is evident.
5 Repeat with different alkali metal salts.

Apparatus
* Bunsen burner
* Heatproof mat
* Range of lithium, sodium and potassium salts in powder/small crystal form and a range in aqueous solutions in (labelled) spray bottles/atomisers.
* Flame test probes/needles
* Small amount of 2 M hydrochloric acid in a watch glass
* Spatula
* Cobalt-blue glass filters

PRACTICAL *contd.*

Spray method

Your technician will have already prepared (labelled) spray bottles with various aqueous solutions of alkali metal salts in them.

Figure 9.10 Spray flame test technique.

1 Spray these directly into the side of a roaring Bunsen burner flame (away from you and other people in the class), from a distance of about 15 cm away from the flame.
2 Observe the reaction and record your observations. You may need to observe the potassium salts through a cobalt-blue filter.
3 Repeat with different alkali metal salts.

Flame probe method

1 Dip the wire end of your flame test probe into the hydrochloric acid and then into one of the alkali metal salt powders, making sure that you have a small quantity of the salt fixed to the metal probe.
2 Place the alkali metal salt on the probe into the hottest part of the Bunsen burner flame.
3 Observe the reaction and record your observation in your table.
4 Repeat with different alkali metal salts. You may need to observe the potassium salts through the cobalt-blue filter.
5 If you have time, your teacher may let you use other metal salts such as copper or calcium.

Figure 9.11 Flame probe experiment.

Analysing your results

1 Were there any differences in the colours of the different alkali metal salts using the three different methods?
2 What were the patterns in the colours produced by:
   a lithium salts?
   b sodium salts?
   c potassium salts?
3 Which method do you think produced the best results? Explain your answer.
4 Explain how you could use this technique to identify any metal ion components of an unknown salt — for example, if a white powder was found at the scene of a crime, how could a flame test help to identify the white powder?

Halogen reactions

You have already seen the reaction of chlorine with lithium and sodium. Chlorine is one of the Group 7 elements, the halogens. The other halogens are shown in Table 9.3.

Table 9.3 Halogens.

Halogen	Symbol (mass number / symbol / atomic number)	Electron structure
Fluorine	$^{19}_{9}F$	2,7
Chlorine	$^{35}_{17}Cl$	2,8,7
Bromine	$^{79}_{35}Br$	2,8,...,7
Iodine	$^{127}_{53}I$	2,8,...,...,7
Astatine	$^{210}_{85}At$	2,8,...,...,...,7

Figure 9.12 Fluorine, chlorine, bromine and iodine

Halogen reactions with iron

Fluorine is a very reactive gas. Iron wool bursts into flames without heating when fluorine gas flows over it. The reaction produces a halide called iron(III) fluoride.

iron + fluorine → iron(III) fluoride

$2Fe(s) + 3F_2(g) \rightarrow \quad 2FeF_3(s)$

In schools we are not allowed to do reactions involving fluorine. Astatine is a radioactive solid, and again, experiments in school involving astatine are not allowed. We can do reactions involving chlorine, bromine and iodine. One of the best ways to see the order of reactivity of the halogens is to react them with iron.

PRACTICAL OBSERVING THE REACTION OF HALOGENS WITH IRON

This activity helps you with:
★ observing and recording observations of reactions
★ using reaction observations to deduce a reactivity series
★ writing balanced chemical equations.

Chlorine, bromine and iodine are all quite hazardous chemicals. Your teacher will demonstrate the reactions of each halogen with iron wool. The experiments will be carried out in a fume cupboard. Observe each reaction and use your observations to deduce the order of reactivity of the halogens.

An excellent description of these reactions and a video demonstrating them can be found at:

www.practicalchemistry.org/experiments/halogen-reactions-with-iron,44, EX.html

Apparatus for demonstration
* reduction tube with iron wool inside
* chlorine generator
* boiling tube with small quantity of liquid bromine in the bottom and iron wool halfway up the tube
* boiling tube with small quantity of iodine in the bottom and iron wool halfway up the tube
* Bunsen burner

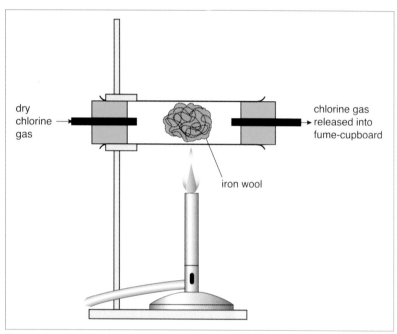

Figure 9.14 Set-up to burn iron in chlorine.

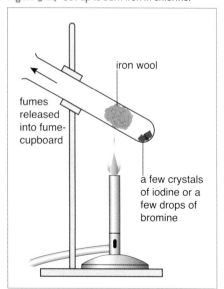

Figure 9.15 Set-up for combustion of bromine/iodine with iron.

continued...

93

(!) Risk assessment

Your teacher will give you a suitable risk assessment for this experiment.

Procedure

Your teacher will demonstrate the reaction of iron with chlorine. Observe the reaction closely and record your observations. Your teacher will then demonstrate the reaction of bromine and then iodine with iron. Record your observations for these reactions as well.

Analysing your results

These questions are about the reactions of the halogens with iron.

1 Which halogen reacted most vigorously with the iron wool?
2 Arrange the three halogens in order of reactivity, from most reactive to least reactive.
3 How does halogen reactivity vary as you go down Group 7?
4 Where would fluorine and astatine be on your halogen reactivity series?
5 Write word and balanced symbol equations for the reaction of chlorine, bromine and iodine with iron.

Halogen displacement reactions

A more reactive halogen can displace a less reactive halogen from a solution of its salts. Chlorine, the second most reactive halogen (after fluorine), will displace both bromine and iodine from solutions of bromides and iodides.

chlorine + sodium bromide $\rightarrow$ bromine + sodium chloride

$$Cl_2(g) + 2NaBr(aq) \rightarrow Br_2(l) + 2NaCl(aq)$$

In the same way, bromine, which is more reactive than iodine, displaces iodine from iodide solutions.

PRACTICAL HALOGEN DISPLACEMENT REACTIONS

This activity helps you with:
★ observing halogen displacement reactions
★ recording experimental observations
★ confirming the halogen reactivity series
★ writing balanced chemical reaction equations.

(!) Risk assessment

Your teacher will give you a risk assessment for this experiment. You must wear safety goggles and do not attempt to smell the contents of the test tubes. Wash the products down the sink after you have performed the reactions and made the observations. Students with asthma should use a fume cupboard if the test tubes are heated.

Procedure

1 Place some dilute sodium or potassium bromide solution in a test tube, and add chlorine water drop by drop, shaking the tube gently.
2 Notice the development of the brownish colour of bromine.
3 Repeat the experiment using dilute sodium or potassium iodide solution.
4 Notice the development of a yellow-brown colour as iodine is formed.
5 If you add too much chlorine water, you may see a grey-black precipitate of iodine form.

continued...

PRACTICAL *contd.*

Apparatus
* chlorine water and dropper
* solutions of potassium bromide, sodium bromide, potassium iodide and sodium iodide
* test tubes and holder
* (for optional teacher demonstration) bromine water
* fume cupboard (if asthmatic)

6 If you warm the contents of the tube gently, you will see the purple colour of iodine vapour.

7 Your teacher may **demonstrate** the displacement of iodine from sodium or potassium iodide solution using bromine water in a fume cupboard.

Questions
These questions are about the displacement of halogens from their halide salts.

1 Will chlorine displace bromine from solutions of metal bromides and iodine from metal iodides?

2 Does reactivity increase or decrease as you go up Group 7 of the Periodic Table? How do the results and observations of the halogen displacement reactions back this up?

3 Write word equations and balanced symbol equations for the displacement of bromine by chlorine from solutions of:
   a sodium bromide
   b potassium bromide

4 Write word equations and balanced symbol equations for the displacement of iodine by **chlorine** and then by **bromine** from solutions of:
   a sodium iodide
   b potassium iodide

5 What would be the reaction between astatine and sodium fluoride?

6 Describe the reaction of fluorine with potassium iodide. What observations would you make? Write word and balanced symbol equations for this reaction.

Identifying halides

Alkali metals can be identified by using a flame test on an unknown salt. If the salt burns with a lilac flame then it contains potassium, and so on. There is a similar way of identifying the halogen element in a halide using a precipitation reaction involving silver nitrate. Chloride, bromide and iodide ions combine with silver ions to form insoluble precipitates of white silver chloride, pale yellow silver bromide and yellow silver iodide, respectively. These reactions form the basis of identifying halide salts.

Silver nitrate contains the silver ion, Ag^+, and the nitrate ion, NO_3^-. Sodium chloride contains the sodium ion, Na^+, and the chloride ion, Cl^-. The important reaction that takes place when the two solutions react is the one between the silver ions and the chloride ions:

$$Ag^+(aq) + Cl^-(aq) \rightarrow AgCl(s)$$

The silver chloride is a solid and precipitates out of solution. The other ions stay in solution.

Adding silver nitrate to solutions of sodium and potassium halides produces precipitation reactions that can be used to identify chlorides, bromides and iodides.

 Risk assessment

Your teacher will give you a risk assessment for this experiment.

Procedure

Testing for a chloride

1 Place 2 cm³ of dilute sodium chloride solution in a test tube.
2 Add 2 cm³ of dilute nitric acid followed by a few drops of dilute silver nitrate solution.
3 A white precipitate of silver chloride should form that turns darker in sunlight and dissolves when dilute ammonia solution is added in excess. This confirms the presence of a chloride.
4 The nitric acid can be left out, but when the solution is an unknown it should be added to prevent other ions such as carbonate and hydroxide interfering with the silver nitrate reaction.

Testing for a bromide

1 Carry this out in exactly the same way as the chloride test above, except use bromides instead of chlorides.
2 A pale yellow precipitate of silver bromide should confirm the presence of bromide. This pale yellow precipitate is insoluble in dilute ammonia solution, but soluble in concentrated ammonia solution.

Testing for an iodide

1 Carry this out in exactly the same way as the chloride test above except use iodides instead of chlorides.
2 A yellow precipitate of silver iodide should confirm the presence of iodide. This yellow precipitate is insoluble in ammonia solution.

Questions

1 What is the test for a chloride?
2 How are the tests for bromides and iodides different from chlorides?
3 When is it important to add nitric acid to the test?
4 Write balanced ionic symbol equations for the bromide test and the iodide test.
5 You are presented with a white solid powder. You suspect that the powder could be either potassium iodide or sodium chloride. Explain the chemical tests that you would perform and the order that you would perform them, to confirm the identity of the unknown white powder.

This activity helps you with:
★ performing the chemical tests for halides
★ observing chemical reactions
★ writing balanced ionic equations.

Apparatus
* Solutions of: sodium chloride; sodium bromide; sodium iodide; potassium chloride; potassium bromide and potassium iodide
* Silver nitrate solution (use sparingly as this chemical is very expensive)
* Teat pipettes
* Test tubes and rack
* Dilute ammonia solution
* Dilute nitric acid

ALKALI METALS AND HALOGENS

PRACTICAL   WHAT'S THE POWDER?

You are given an unknown white powder – it may not be the same as the powder given to other people in your class. It is suspected to be an alkali metal halide. Design and plan a sequence of chemical tests to identify the white powder; include a flow diagram showing how you will do the tests. Produce a list of apparatus that you will require and give this to your teacher or technician to organise the necessary equipment and chemicals. Write a risk assessment for this practical – your teacher will give you a suitable blank risk assessment form and any necessary Hazcards. Perform the practical and identify the white powder. Confirm the name of the white powder with your teacher or science technician. Did you get it right?

Chapter summary

○ The reactions of Group 1 metals (the alkali metals) with the following can be investigated in order to establish the trend in reactivity within the group:
  ● oxygen in the air (corrosion of newly exposed surface and burning)
  ● water
  ● Group 7 elements
○ Lithium, sodium and potassium react with water.
○ The reactions of Group 7 elements (the halogens) with iron can be investigated in order to establish the trend in reactivity within the group.
○ There are trends in reactivity within Group 1 and Group 7 and word and balanced symbol equations for the above reactions can be written and interpreted.
○ The displacement reactions of Group 7 elements can be investigated in order to:
  ● confirm the trend in reactivity within the group
  ● make predictions based on this trend
  ● write and interpret word and balanced symbol equations for the reactions.
○ Flame tests detect the presence of lithium, sodium and potassium ions.
○ Silver nitrate solution can be used to detect the presence of chloride, bromide and iodide ions.
○ There are ionic equations for these reactions.
○ The above tests can be used in problem-solving situations to plan and carry out procedures to identify substances.

10 Chemical bonding, structure and properties

In this chapter we will discover how the properties of materials are related to their structure and why it is that different materials have different properties. We are going to start by looking at four common groups of materials.

Figure 10.1 Copper, sodium chloride, water, diamond and graphite.

FACTFILE   COPPER – A METAL

Physical properties

- **High electrical conductivity** – electric current easily passes through copper wires.
- **High thermal conductivity** – copper is usually used for heat exchangers inside boilers and for pots and pans.
- **High melting and boiling point** – copper can be used for high temperature applications like pots, pans and central heating components.
- **Ductile** – copper can be easily drawn into wires.
- **Malleable** – copper can be easily hammered or squashed into different permanent shapes, such as pots, pans and plumbing components.
- **Corrosion resistant** – copper is very low in the metal reactivity series and doesn't corrode easily.
- **Antibacterial** – copper inhibits the growth of many different types of bacteria making it very useful in food preparation and water systems.
- **Tough** – copper does not fracture easily when it is stressed, making it useful for tools.
- **Non-magnetic** – copper cannot be magnetised, which makes it very useful for specialised tools and military applications.
- **Easy to alloy** – copper forms alloys easily with other metals. It makes brass when alloyed with zinc, it makes bronze when alloyed with tin and it makes cupronickel when alloyed with nickel; all of these alloys have many useful properties.
- **Attractive colour** – copper and its alloys have attractive, shiny, non-tarnishing surfaces making them useful for ornaments and jewellery.
- **Recyclable** – copper can be recycled without affecting any of its properties. Over 40% of copper sold on the global market is recycled. Recycled copper commands about 95% of the price of new copper.
- Copper has many of the classical properties associated with metals. Its main failing is its lack of **strength**. Because it is ductile and malleable, it is quite easily deformed; this means that copper is not a very good structural metal, unlike steel (which is very strong).

Structure of copper

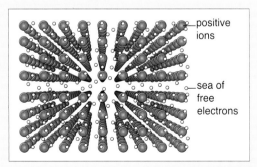

Figure 10.2 Metallic structure of copper.

Solid copper, like all solid metals, has a structure consisting of a **lattice** (regular 3-dimensional array) of **positive ions** through which a '**sea**' of **free electrons** are free to move. The positive ions and the 'sea' of electrons interact to form metallic bonds. The free electrons are the outermost electrons on the

continued...

copper atoms, which are stripped from the atoms when they freeze together to make the solid copper; the rest of the atom forms the positive ion cores.

Explaining the main physical properties using the structural model
The lattice/free electron model explains the high electrical and thermal conductivity of metals including copper. The sea of free electrons can easily move throughout the structure of the metal. Electrons carry a negative charge, so electric current is the movement of the free electrons through the structure – from negative to positive. The positive ions are close together and bonded by metallic bonds. The structure can easily pass the vibration of hot particles from one particle to the next particle; also the free electrons can move faster as they are heated and transfer the heat from hot to cold throughout the structure – this explains why metals are good thermal conductors. The arrangement of the positive ions in copper and the number of free electrons makes copper a particularly good conductor of electricity and heat.

Discussion Point

Your teacher may show you an animation of conduction of electricity in a metal. How does the conductivity of a metal change with temperature, the dimensions of the wire and the material that the wire is made of?

QUESTIONS

1 What are the two most important properties of metals?
2 What properties make copper such a good material for making water pipes?
3 Why are electrical connecting wires made out of strands of copper?
4 Why are metals such good conductors of electricity?
5 Describe how the 'positive ion/free electron' model of copper can be used to explain its physical properties:
   a High melting and boiling point
   b Ductility
   c Malleability
   d Toughness

FACTFILE   SODIUM CHLORIDE (COMMON SALT) – AN IONIC COMPOUND

Figure 10.3 Salt crystals.

Physical properties
- **High melting point.**
- **Solid** sodium chloride **does not conduct electricity**.
- **Molten or aqueous** (dissolved in water) sodium chloride **does conduct electricity** – sodium chloride is often used as an electrolyte in chemical cells.
- **Soluble in water** (insoluble in organic solvents) – sodium chloride is used as a flavouring and preservative in food.
- **Brittle**.

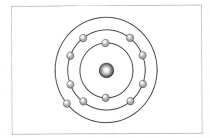

Figure 10.4 Sodium atom.

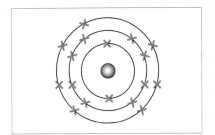

Figure 10.5 Chlorine atom.

Structure of sodium chloride

Sodium chloride is a classic example of an ionic compound. An atom of sodium has the electron configuration 2,8,1 (see Figure 10.4). An atom of chlorine has the electron configuration 2,8,7 (see Figure 10.5).

When sodium reacts with chlorine to make sodium chloride, the sodium atom will want to lose its outermost electron (to make its electron configuration the same as that of the noble gas neon), and chlorine will want to gain an electron (to make its electron configuration the same as that of the noble gas argon – noble gases have particularly stable electron configurations). The sodium atom will become a sodium ion, Na^+ (because it has lost an electron), and the chlorine atom will become a chloride ion, Cl^- (because it has gained an electron). Figure 10.6 shows this process.

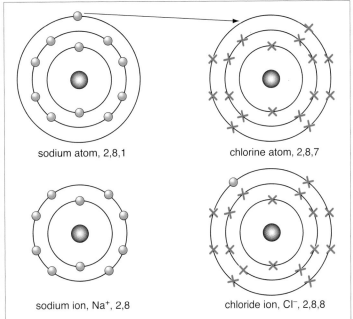

sodium atom, 2,8,1   chlorine atom, 2,8,7

sodium ion, Na^+, 2,8   chloride ion, Cl^-, 2,8,8

Figure 10.6 Formation of sodium chloride by electron transfer.

The salt, sodium chloride, contains positively charged sodium ions and negatively charged chloride ions. Since solid sodium chloride is electrically neutral, there must be equal numbers of sodium and chloride ions. The total positive charges cancel out the total negative charges. The formula for sodium chloride is NaCl. Positive charges attract negative charges strongly (this is called **electrostatic attraction**), and the millions of sodium and chloride ions in a crystal of sodium chloride are held together in a regular 3-dimensional lattice (a regular, repeating structure) by these strong electrostatic forces (see Figures 10.7 and 10.8).

The ions in sodium chloride crystals are arranged in a **cubic** lattice, each ion being surrounded by six nearest neighbours of opposite charge – they form the corners of a cube. This is shown in Figure 10.7. The simplest way of drawing the arrangement of the ions in the lattice is shown in Figure 10.8 – this is called the **unit cell** of sodium chloride.

continued...

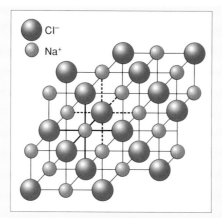

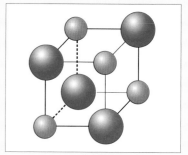

Figure 10.8 Part of the sodium chloride lattice.

Figure 10.7 Sodium chloride lattice of ions.

Explaining the main physical properties using the structural model

The high melting points of ionic compounds, and sodium chloride in particular, can be explained by the fact that the sodium and chloride ions have very strong attractive electrostatic forces between them which need a lot of energy to overcome them. This energy can be provided by heating, but high temperatures are needed to supply enough energy to break the electrostatic bonds. Solid ionic compounds do not conduct electricity because the sodium and chloride ions are held in fixed positions within their lattice and are not free to move. If there are no moving charged particles, there will be no electrical conduction. When molten or dissolved in water, ionic compounds do conduct electricity because the lattice breaks down, and the ions are free to move – the moving ions create an electrical current.

Brittleness is a typical property of ionic substances. If a stress is applied to a crystal, which shifts the ion layers slightly, the ion layers will tend to jump over each other (Figure 10.9). Ions of the same charge are then brought side by side and so repel each other. The crystal fractures rather than stretches.

Figure 10.9 Salt is brittle.

Discussion Point

Salt is incredibly important to us as human beings. Find out why our bodies rely on salt so much and why it is important to regulate the amount of salt that we consume in our food.

QUESTIONS

6 How are sodium and chloride **ions** formed from sodium and chlorine **atoms**?
7 Why is sodium chloride (common salt) used as a flavouring and preservative for food?
8 Explain why sodium chloride crystals are brittle.
9 What happens when sodium chloride crystals are added to water?
10 Molten and solid sodium chloride contain the same sodium and chloride ions. Why does molten sodium chloride conduct electricity, while solid sodium chloride does not conduct electricity?
11 Calcium oxide is another ionic compound. Calcium has two electrons in its outer shell, and oxygen has six electrons in its outer shell. Draw dot and cross diagrams to show how calcium oxide is formed by electron transfer from calcium to oxygen atoms.
12 Draw dot and cross diagrams to show the formation of:
   a Lithium fluoride from lithium and fluorine
   b Sodium sulfide from sodium and sulfur
   c Magnesium chloride from magnesium and chlorine.

FACTFILE   WATER – A SIMPLE COVALENT MOLECULE

Figure 10.10 Water as a solid, a liquid and a gas (ice, water and steam).

Physical properties

- **Low melting (and boiling) point.**
- **Liquid at room temperature** – most simple covalent molecules are gases or liquids at room temperature.
- **Poor conductor of electricity** – most simple covalent molecules are non-conductors.
- **Excellent solvent** – most simple covalent molecules are soluble in water.

Structure of water

Water is an example of a covalent molecular compound, all of which exist as neutral particles called molecules. Molecules are formed from atoms when they share electrons. A covalent bond forms when a pair of electrons is shared between two atoms. When water molecules form as hydrogen reacts with oxygen, two atoms of hydrogen combine with one atom of oxygen. Hydrogen has one electron in its outer shell, and needs one more to get two (the same number as the noble gas helium). Oxygen has six electrons in its outer shell and needs to get two more to get the same number as the noble gas neon.

Figure 10.11 shows the dot and cross diagram for hydrogen and oxygen forming water. The oxygen atom and the two hydrogen atoms share electrons – each atom then has a full outer electron shell.

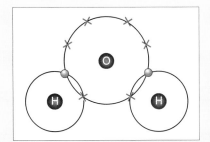

Figure 10.11 A water molecule.

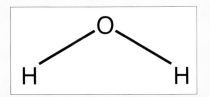

Figure 10.12 Structural formula of water.

Explaining the main physical properties using the structural model

The covalent bond is a pair of electrons shared between two atoms. Covalent bonds are very strong. It takes a lot of energy to break them. The molecules themselves, however, attract each other only very weakly as each molecule is overall neutral. This means that solid covalent substances have low melting points, because very little energy is required to separate the molecules and turn the solid to a liquid. The weakness of these intermolecular forces explains why so many covalent compounds like water are liquids or gases at room temperature. Covalent bonds are usually represented by a line between the atoms, illustrating where the bond is. This type of diagram is called a structural formula, and although the molecules themselves are 3-dimensional, structural formulae are normally drawn in two dimensions. The structural formula of water is shown in Figure 10.12.

Discussion Point

Water is an unusual molecule in many ways. Find out some of the properties of water that make it different from other simple molecular compounds. For example, why does water conduct electricity at all, and why does ice float?

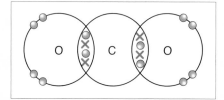
QUESTIONS

13 What is a covalent bond?

14 How is water formed from hydrogen and oxygen?

15 Why is water a liquid at room temperature?

16 Why is water only a poor conductor of electricity?

17 Draw dot and cross diagrams showing the covalent bonds in the following molecules:

   a hydrogen chloride

   b ammonia

   c methane

18 Some atoms can form double covalent bonds. In these molecules, each atom shares four electrons (in two pairs). Carbon dioxide is an example of a molecule containing double covalent bonds:

Draw dot and cross diagrams and structural formulae for the following molecules containing double covalent bonds:

a sulfur dioxide

b oxygen gas

FACTFILE **DIAMOND AND GRAPHITE – GIANT COVALENT SUBSTANCES**

Figure 10.13 Diamond and graphite.

Table 10.1 Physical properties of diamond and graphite.

Physical properties of diamond	Physical properties of graphite
Transparent and crystalline – used as a gemstone in jewellery	**Grey/black shiny solid**
Extremely hard – used for glass cutting, small industrial diamonds are used in drill bits for oil exploration etc.	**Very soft** – used as a lubricant and used in pencils (the softer the pencil, the more graphite there is in the 'lead')
Electrical insulator	Is a **non-metal that conducts electricity**. Graphite is used for electrodes in some manufacturing processes
Very high melting point, over 3500 °C	**Very high melting point**, over 3600 °C

FACTFILE *contd.*

The structure of diamond and graphite

Some covalent substances exist as giant structures that have high melting points because all the atoms are held together by very strong covalent bonds. Graphite and diamond are examples of giant covalent structures. Diamond and graphite are both different physical forms of carbon – these are called **allotropes** (different physical forms of the same substance). Both diamond and graphite contain covalent bonds between carbon atoms.

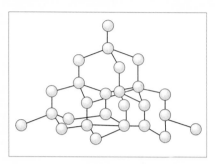

Figure 10.14 The structure of diamond.

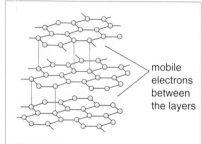

mobile electrons between the layers

Figure 10.15 The structure of graphite.

The carbon atoms in diamond are each connected to four other carbon atoms by a strong covalent bond. The structure is a 3-dimensional lattice based on a tetrahedral unit cell, each carbon atom at the corner of a tetrahedron (see Figure 10.16).

Graphite, in contrast, is made up of layers of carbon atoms, arranged in hexagonal rings. Each carbon atom forms a strong covalent bond with three others in the same layer. However, the bonds between the layers are quite weak and allow the hexagonal-ring layers to slide over one another.

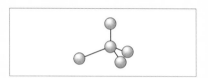

Figure 10.16 Tetrahedral diamond unit cell.

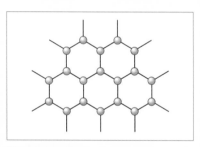

Figure 10.17 Hexagonal layer structure of graphite.

Explaining the main physical properties using the structural models

The carbon atoms in the layers of graphite are held together by three strong covalent bonds, forming the hexagonal-ring layer. Carbon is a Group 4 element and so it has four outer electrons; it needs to share four other electrons to get a complete outer electron shell. It gets three of these electrons from the carbon atoms in the hexagonal ring. The fourth electron from each atom, which is not used in bonding **within** the layers, joins a delocalised system of electrons **between** the layers of carbon atoms. Graphite conducts electricity quite well along the layers because it has charged electrons that are free to move, forming an electric current. Graphite does not conduct electricity across the layers. The hexagonal layers in graphite can slide over one another (because the bonds between the layers are very weak), giving graphite its slippery feel and lubricating properties. The carbon atoms are held together by strong covalent bonds, so that heat has little physical effect on graphite and its melting point is high.

In diamond, all four of the outer electrons are involved in covalent bonding with four other carbon atoms. The result is a giant rigid covalent structure. There are no free electrons to conduct electricity. This gives diamond its incredible hardness and high melting point, as a lot of energy is required to break down the lattice. Unlike graphite, diamond is a transparent material.

Discussion Point

Allotropes can be found in other elements as well. Find out about the different allotrope forms of:
- phosphorus
- oxygen
- sulfur
- tin

PRACTICAL | MAKING MOLECULAR MODELS

This activity helps you with:
★ making structural models of materials.

Your teacher will give you a molecular modelling kit such as a Molymod® kit. Your task is to use the kit to make examples of the following materials:

1 A sodium chloride unit cell

2 A diamond unit cell

3 A hexagonal graphite unit cell

For each structure draw a labelled diagram, illustrating the component parts.

Carbon nanotubes

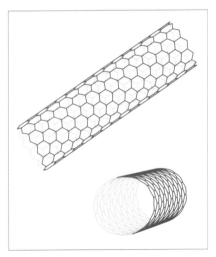

Figure 10.18 Carbon nanotubes.

Carbon nanotubes are another allotrope of carbon. They are molecular-scale tubes of graphite-like carbon with remarkable properties. Carbon nanotubes are among the stiffest and strongest fibres known to mankind (they can be five times stronger than steel) and they have amazing electronic properties: depending on their exact structure they can have higher electrical conductivity than copper – all in a tube about 10 000 times thinner than a human hair.

Carbon nanotubes are formed when graphite layers form and then roll up into tubes rather than being deposited in layers. The covalently-bonded hexagonal carbon sheets make carbon nanotubes incredibly strong and the free electrons give them a high electrical conductivity. One of the proposed uses of carbon nanotubes is for connections inside miniature electronic circuits. As electronic circuitry gets smaller, conventional connections are not practical, and nanotube technology may be the answer. The problem at the moment is to arrange many thousands of nanotubes in a defined pattern to make a circuit – current technology does not allow us to do this. Most of the current applications of carbon nanotubes are based on their strength.

Bulk materials are made out of a mass of nanotubes for use in bicycle components, boat hulls and epoxy-resins for bonding high performance components in wind-turbines and sports equipment.

Carbon nanotubes have also been used in atomic force microscopes, bone-tissue scaffolding and in cancer treatment.

Figure 10.19 A bicycle made from carbon nanotubes.

QUESTIONS

24 What are carbon nanotubes?

25 Why are materials made from carbon nanotubes a good choice for components on a bike?

26 Why do carbon nanotubes conduct electricity? How could they be made into electrical connections inside electronic devices?

Discussion Point

Carbon nanotubes are definitely a material for the future — can you think of any good applications for a very lightweight, incredibly strong, electrically conducting material?

Smart materials

What are smart materials? Why use the word 'smart'? Smart materials have properties which change reversibly with a change in their surroundings. Smart pigments, for example, that are used in some paint applications, change their colour.

Thermochromic pigments are materials that form the basis of special paints that change their colour at a specific temperature.

Figure 10.20 Thermochromic paint applications, the kettle changes colour as it gets hot.

Most thermochromic materials are based on liquid crystal technology, similar to the materials used in flat screen televisions. At specific temperatures, the liquid crystals re-orientate themselves to produce an apparent change in colour. When the temperature drops, they re-orientate back into their original shape and colour. Thermochromic pigments have been used in mugs that change colour when they have hot liquids in them, battery power indicators and T-shirts that change colour depending on body temperature!

Photochromic pigments change colour with light intensity. Photochromic pigments contain special organic molecules that, when exposed to light, particularly ultraviolet light, change colour. The light breaks a bond in the molecule, which then rearranges itself, forming a molecule with a different colour. When the light source is removed, the molecule returns to its original form. Manufacturers usually offer four basic colours – violet, blue, yellow and red – from which other colours can be made by mixing.

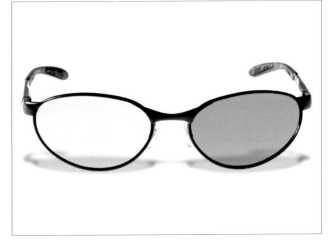

Figure 10.21 Photochromic T-shirts and lenses.

Photochromic pigments have been used in T-shirt design, but perhaps the most wide-scale application is for photochromic lenses in glasses (Figure 10.21).

Shape-memory polymers are 'plastics' that can regain their shape when they are heated. These polymers are somewhere between thermoplastics and thermosets. When first heated, the polymer softens, and it can be stretched or deformed – or pressed into a particular shape by a machine. On cooling, it remains in the deformed, changed-shape state. On being reheated, it 'remembers' its original shape, to which it returns. This property is called shape retention. Shape-memory polymers are used in the building industry for sealing around window frames and for the manufacture of sportswear such as helmets and gum-shields.

Potential applications are plastic car bodies from which a dent could be removed by heating, and medical sutures ('stitches') that will automatically adjust to the correct tension and be biodegradable, and so will not need to be surgically removed.

Shape-memory alloys are metal alloys that also regain their original shape when they are heated (like shape-memory polymers). Some alloys, in particular some nickel/titanium alloys (often called NiTi or nitinol) and copper/aluminium/nickel alloys, have two remarkable properties: pseudoelasticity (they appear to be elastic), and shape-retention (when deformed, they return to their original shape after heating).

Applications include: deformable spectacle frames (Figure 10.22); surgical plates for joining bone fractures (as the body warms the plates, they put more tension on the bone fracture than conventional plates); surgical wires that replace tendons; thermostats for electrical devices such as coffee pots; and in the aeronautical industry, for example, shape-memory alloy wires can be heated by an electric current and made to operate wing-flaps as an alternative to the conventional hydraulic systems.

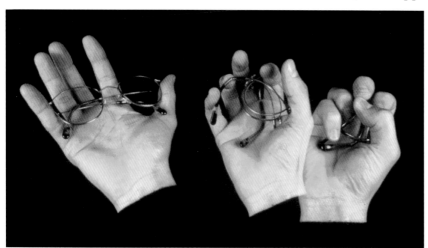

Figure 10.22 Deformable spectacles.

Hydrogels are polymers that absorb or expel water and swell or shrink (up to 1000 times their volume) due to changes in pH or temperature. Hydrogels are cross-linked polymers that, due to the open nature of the cross-linked structure, enable water (or some aqueous solutions) to be absorbed within the structure causing the structure to swell. Small changes in the stimulus (either temperature or pH) control the amount of swelling or shrinking.

Applications include: artificial muscles; underground water cut-off in the oil industry (the volume of gel can be pH-controlled); robotic actuators (found in some cases to be more effective than shape-memory alloys); and houses threatened by forest fires where hydrogels can be more effective than fire-fighting foam.

QUESTIONS

27 What is a 'smart material'?
28 Explain the difference between:
    a a **thermochromic** pigment and a **photochromic** pigment
    b a shape-memory **polymer** and a shape-memory **alloy**
29 How can hydrogels be made to absorb more or less water?
30 Explain why smart materials are used to manufacture:
    a photochromic flexi glasses
    b sport gum-shields
    c battery power indicators
    d novelty T-shirts

Chapter summary

○ Metals, ionic compounds, simple molecular covalent substances and giant covalent substances have different properties.

○ The 'sea' of electrons/lattice of positive ions structural model for metals can be used to explain their physical properties.

○ The electronic structure of atoms can help to explain how ions are formed.

○ Dot and cross diagrams can show how ionic bonding takes place in simple binary compounds formed from Group 1 or 2 elements and elements from Group 6 or 7.

○ The accepted structural model for giant ionic structures explains the physical properties of ionic substances.

○ The electronic structure of atoms can help explain how covalent bonds are formed.

○ Dot and cross diagrams can show the covalent bonding in simple molecules, including examples which contain double bonds.

○ The intermolecular bonding structural model for simple molecular structures can help explain the physical properties of simple molecular substances.

○ The structures and properties of diamond, graphite and carbon nanotubes can be described and discussed in terms of their bonding and structure.

○ The properties and uses of carbon nanotubes are related to their bonding and structure.

○ Thermochromic pigments, photochromic pigments, hydrogels, shape-memory alloys and shape-memory polymers are known as smart materials and have properties which change reversibly with a change in their surroundings:
  ● thermochromic pigments change colour with changing temperature
  ● photochromic pigments change colour with changing light intensity
  ● hydrogels absorb/expel water and swell/shrink (up to 1000 times their volume) due to changes in pH or temperature
  ● shape-memory alloys regain their original shape when heated
  ● shape-memory polymers regain their original shape when heated.

○ The uses of smart materials depend on their properties.

11 Rates of reaction and chemical calculations

The manufacture of chemicals on large, industrial scales takes time and money. In fact, in the chemical industry, time is money! In general, the faster that a chemical is made, the more profitable it is, but it is also important to take into account lots of other factors such as energy requirements, availability of materials, plant and workforce and the current state of the economic market. Chemists and engineers spend a great deal of time and effort analysing chemical reactions to make sure that reactions are occurring the way that they want them to (to ensure they get the correct product) and that the manufacturing conditions are optimised to deliver the maximum amount of product in the shortest period of time.

Figure 11.1 A large-scale chemical plant in Billingham, Teeside.

Measuring the rate of a reaction

There are many ways to measure the rate of a reaction. By rate we mean, 'how much product is produced in a set time' (usually per second). The rate of a reaction can be determined by measuring the amount of product produced (usually by mass or volume) over time. By studying the graph of amount of product against time, we can determine the rate of the reaction by measuring the gradient or slope of the graph – this tells us how much product is being produced per unit time.

There are three simple ways of measuring rates of reaction in a school laboratory:

- Capture and measure the volume of gas produced by a reaction.
- Measure and record the change in mass of a reaction.
- Measure and record the amount of light passing through a chemical reaction (e.g. as it is producing a precipitate).

This activity helps you with:
★ working as part of a team
★ producing a risk assessment
★ measuring the rate of chemical reactions
★ comparing different methods of measuring the rates of chemical reactions.

Measuring reactions involving gases

Chemical reactions involving the release of a gas are quite straightforward to study. The rate of the reaction can be determined by analysing the results of experiments where the volume of gas produced is measured against time.

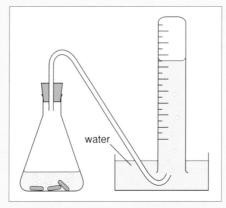

water

Figure 11.2 The reaction between calcium carbonate and hydrochloric acid in which carbon dioxide is formed, in a graduated tube.

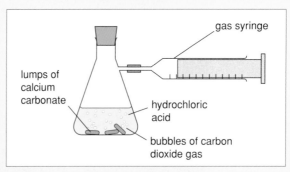

gas syringe

lumps of calcium carbonate

hydrochloric acid

bubbles of carbon dioxide gas

Figure 11.3 The same reaction, in a gas syringe.

In this practical, the reaction that you are going to study is the reaction of calcium carbonate with hydrochloric acid forming calcium chloride, water and carbon dioxide gas.

calcium carbonate + hydrochloric acid → calcium chloride + water + carbon dioxide

$$CaCO_3(s) \quad + \quad 2HCl(aq) \quad \rightarrow \quad CaCl_2(aq) \quad + H_2O(l) + \quad CO_2(g)$$

Your teacher will give you a blank risk assessment form and any appropriate CLEAPSS guidance to enable you to complete a risk assessment for these experiments.

You will measure the amount of gas produced in two ways:
• by displacement of water
• using a gas syringe.

PRACTICAL contd.

Apparatus
* calcium carbonate chips
* dilute hydrochloric acid
* conical flask
* gas delivery tube and bung
* graduated tube (inverted measuring cylinder/burette)
* water bath with beehive shelf
* side-arm conical flask (Büchner flask) with delivery tube
* gas syringe with stand, clamp and boss
* stop watch

Procedure
1 Make a table to record the volume of gas produced every 30 s for about 5 minutes (for both methods).
2 Your teacher will tell you approximate quantities to use for each experiment.
3 Set up the apparatus as shown in Figure 11.2.
4 Place the calcium carbonate chips into the flask, pour in the hydrochloric acid and quickly replace the stopper. **Start the stop watch.**
5 Measure and record the volume of gas produced in the graduated tube every 30 seconds.
6 Continue until the graduated tube is full of gas or until the amount of gas produced does not change for 1 minute.
7 Repeat the experiment using the apparatus in Figure 11.3.

Analysing your results and measuring the rate of reaction
Plot a graph of volume of gas produced against time for each method – try to plot them on the same scaled axes. Your graph (for one of the experiments) should look like Figure 11.4.

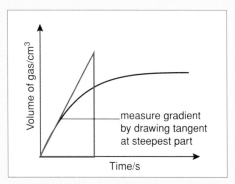

Figure 11.4 The rate at which a gas is given off.

1 What is the shape of your graph?
2 What does your graph tell you? Where is the rate of reaction fastest?
3 Can you tell when the reaction is complete?
4 Calculate the rate of reaction at the steepest part of your graph by drawing a tangent line and measuring the gradient (the units will be cm^3/s).
5 Repeat the rate of reaction calculation for both methods. Are the rates of reaction the same? Should they be the same? Why might the two rates be different?

Measuring reactions involving changes of mass
The same chemical reaction can be measured using a method based on measuring the mass of the reactants. As carbon dioxide gas is given off by the reaction it will escape from the conical flask and the mass of flask and reactants will drop. By plotting a graph of mass against time, the rate of reaction can be calculated by measuring the gradient of the mass curve at any time.

continued...

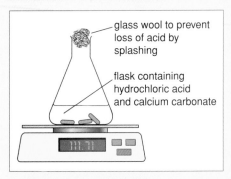

Figure 11.5 Flask being weighed.

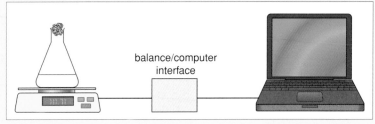

Figure 11.6 Datalogging the loss of mass.

Apparatus
* calcium carbonate chips
* dilute hydrochloric acid
* flask
* ceramic wool stopper
* stop watch
* electronic balance
* (optional) datalogger, computer and datalogging software

Procedure
1 Construct a table to record the mass of the flask and contents every 30 s for about 5 minutes.
2 Your teacher will tell you the amounts to use.
3 Set the apparatus up as in Figure 11.5, or Figure 11.6 if using the optional datalogger equipment.
4 This experiment is better started by adding the calcium carbonate chips to the acid and then plugging the flask with a ceramic wool stopper (to prevent splashing).
5 Measure and record the mass of the system every 30 s for about 5 minutes.
6 Continue until the mass of the flask and contents does not change for about 1 minute.

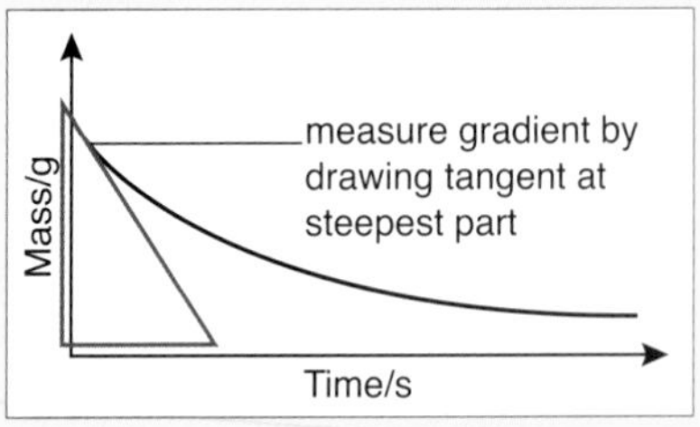

Analysing your results and measuring the rate of reaction
Plot a graph of mass of flask and contents against time, or download the datalogged version. Your graph should look like the one shown in Figure 11.7.
6 What is the shape of your graph?
7 What does your graph tell you? Where is the rate of reaction fastest?
8 Can you tell when the reaction is complete?
9 Calculate the rate of reaction at the steepest part of your graph by drawing a tangent line and measuring the gradient (the units will be g/s).

Figure 11.7 Graph of total mass against time.

Apparatus
* Sodium thiosulfate solution
* Dilute hydrochloric acid
* Syringe
* Flask
* Light shield (black paper)
* Tripod
* Stand, bosses × 2, clamps × 2
* Mains lightbulb and holder
* Light sensor and meter
* Stop watch
* (Optional) datalogger, computer, datalogging software

Measuring reactions involving changes of light transmission through a precipitate
In this reaction sodium thiosulfate reacts with hydrochloric acid forming solid (yellow) sulfur. The rate of the reaction can be measured by recording the transmission of light through the solution as the sulfur precipitate gradually forms, making the solution cloudier and cloudier. The transmission of light can be measured using a datalogger and light sensor. By plotting a graph of intensity of transmitted light against time, the rate of reaction at any time can be calculated by measuring the gradient of the curve. The reaction can be summarised by the equation:

$$\text{sodium thiosulfate} + \text{hydrochloric acid} \rightarrow \text{sodium chloride} + \text{water} + \text{sulfur dioxide} + \text{sulfur}$$

$$Na_2S_2O_3(aq) + 2HCl(aq) \rightarrow 2NaCl(aq) + H_2O(l) + SO_2(g) + S(s)$$

PRACTICAL *contd.*

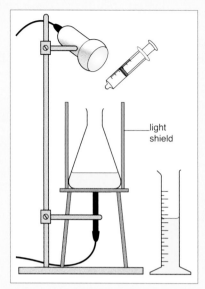

Figure 11.8 Measuring changes in light transmission through a precipitate.

Procedure

1 Construct a table to record your results – you will need to record the light intensity every 30 s for about 5 minutes.
2 Set up the apparatus as shown in Figure 11.8.
3 Your teacher will tell you the amounts of each chemical to use.
4 Add the hydrochloric acid to the sodium thiosulfate solution using the syringe.
5 Measure and record the transmitted light intensity every 30 s for about 5 minutes (or use the optional datalogger and software).

Analysing your results

Plot a graph of light intensity against time, or download the datalogged version. Your graph should look like the one shown in Figure 11.9.

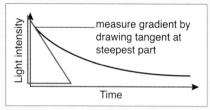

Figure 11.9 Graph of light intensity against time.

10 What is the pattern/shape of your graph?
11 What does your graph tell you? Where is the rate of reaction fastest?
12 Can you tell when the reaction is complete?

QUESTIONS

1 What is meant by the **rate** of a reaction?
2 Explain how you use a graph to measure the rate of a reaction.
3 How can you tell from a rate of reaction graph where the reaction is:
   a fastest?
   b complete?
4 In a calcium carbonate and hydrochloric acid experiment, a student collects the carbon dioxide gas and produces the rate of reaction graph shown in Figure 11.10. On a copy of this graph, sketch the graph you would expect from similar experiments carried out with:
   a acid of twice the concentration, but at the same temperature
   b the same amount of each chemical, but carried out at a higher temperature.
   Explain your sketches.

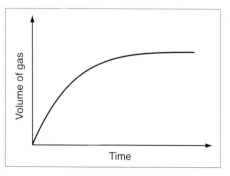

Figure 11.10

Explaining the rate of a reaction

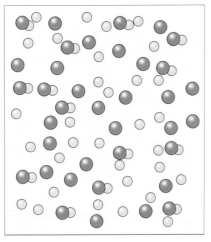

Figure 11.11 Moving gas particles move randomly.

A chemical reaction occurs when the reacting molecules, atoms or ions collide with one another. Not all collisions result in a chemical reaction, but when the collision has enough energy for bonds to break and be reformed, then a reaction can take place. The number of successful collisions is a small percentage of the total number of collisions taking place in a given time – the number of successful collisions per second is called the collision frequency. The higher the collision frequency, the higher the rate of reaction.

The easiest reactions to visualise are those that take place between gases. Particles of each gas are in constant random motion, colliding with each other, the walls of the containing vessel, and crucially, with particles of the other gas.

Figure 11.11 shows particles of two different reacting gases (shown in yellow and red). All the particles are moving at high speed in random directions. When one of the red particles collides with one of the yellow particles with enough energy, then the reaction will occur.

Factors that affect the rate of a chemical reaction

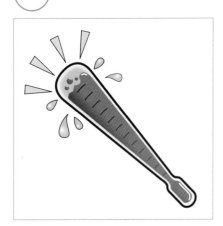

1 The temperature of the reaction – a higher temperature means a higher rate of reaction

Increasing the temperature of a reaction increases the average velocity of the particles. If the particles are moving faster, then they are likely to collide with enough energy more frequently – the collision frequency increases. A higher collision frequency means a higher rate of reaction. The reaction will be quicker. For many reactions, a 10 °C rise in temperature doubles the rate of reaction.

2 The concentration of the reactants – a higher concentration means a higher rate of reaction

Increasing the concentration of the reactants effectively increases the total number of reacting particles in the same volume. If there are more particles then there are likely to be more collisions with enough energy – the collision frequency increases, as does the rate of reaction.

Figure 11.12

3 The surface area of the reactants – a higher surface area means a higher rate of reaction

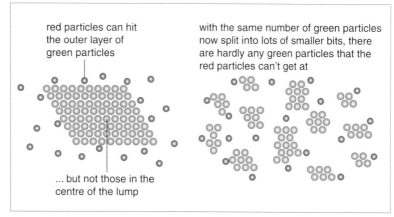

red particles can hit the outer layer of green particles

with the same number of green particles now split into lots of smaller bits, there are hardly any green particles that the red particles can't get at

... but not those in the centre of the lump

Figure 11.13

Figure 11.13 shows that when one of the reactants is in a large lump, then the other reactant cannot react with any of the particles in the middle of the lump. When the lump is broken up, **increasing the surface area**, then more of the reactants can collide with each other with enough energy, increasing the collision frequency and the rate of reaction. The larger the surface area, the higher the rate of reaction – or put another way, powdered reactants react at a faster rate than lumps of reactants!

4 Using a catalyst – a catalyst can increase the rate of reaction

Catalysts are substances that increase the rate of a chemical reaction but remain chemically unchanged at the end of the reaction.

Many catalysts work only for one particular reaction and some industrial reactions are only possible on large scales by using a catalyst.

A catalyst works because it provides a 'surface' on which the reacting molecules can collide with each other – this reduces the amount of energy needed for a collision to be successful. Lower energy means more particles will be able to react in a set time, increasing the collision frequency and increasing the rate of reaction.

Although some reactions only take place with one specific catalyst, some materials act as catalysts for many different reactions.

The importance of catalysts

Chemists and chemical engineers estimate that 90% of all chemical products produced commercially involve catalysts at some stage in the process of their manufacture. Catalysts are used in the production of bulk chemicals, such as sulfuric acid, ammonia and polymers; fine chemicals, such as dyes and medicines; petrochemicals, such as petrol and diesel; and in food processing, particularly in the production of margarine. In 2005, catalysts were involved in the production of over £500 billion worth of chemical products worldwide, equivalent to the entire gross domestic product (GDP) of Australia!

The use of catalysts in chemical processes has huge importance not only in terms of economic factors. Catalysts reduce the amount of energy required to produce chemical products which in turn preserves world fuel reserves and also reduces the environmental impact of burning fossil fuels and its effect on the greenhouse effect and global warming.

Ammonia is produced using catalysts in a reaction called the Haber Process.

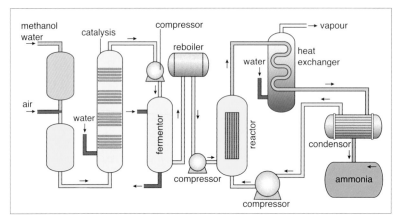

Figure 11.14 The Haber Process.

Ammonia is used to produce over 100 million tonnes of nitrogen-rich plant fertiliser each year, contributing to feeding over one third of the world's population. The most common catalysts for the production of ammonia via the Haber Process are the metal elements iron and ruthenium. Without the catalysts, the reaction is so slow that virtually no reaction takes place within any sensible, industrial timescale, so about 2.3 billion people in the world rely on the plant fertiliser produced from ammonia through the action of catalysts in the Haber Process.

Discussion Point

The Haber Process is incredibly important to the whole of the world's population. Not only is a catalyst used for the reaction between nitrogen and hydrogen, but the process is optimised by adjusting the temperature and pressure of the reaction.
Your teacher will show you an animation of the process where you can adjust the temperature and pressure of the reaction. Find out the conditions to produce the optimum yield.
www.freezeray.com/flashFiles/theHaberProcess.htm

QUESTIONS

5 What is a catalyst?
6 How can the rate of reaction of calcium carbonate with hydrochloric acid be increased?
7 When magnesium reacts with hydrochloric acid, hydrogen gas is produced. In a particular experiment at 20 °C, 50 cm³ of hydrogen gas was produced in 3 minutes. What would be the result of the reaction if the same quantities of reactant were used but the reaction was carried out at 30 °C?
8 Why is it important to a chemical company to increase the yield of a reaction?
9 Why is it important for the environment to use catalysts in the production of chemicals?

TASK — SIMULATING RATES OF REACTION

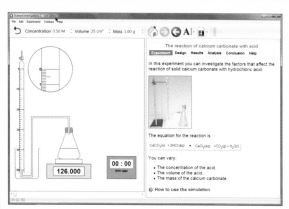

Figure 11.15 A scientific rate of reaction simulator.
Reproduced courtesy of Focus Educational Software Ltd.

There are many scientific software simulations that allow you to investigate the factors that affect the rate of a reaction. You will use one of these simulations (or your teacher will demonstrate one to you) to model a particular reaction. You must investigate all four of the factors that affect the rate of a reaction: temperature, surface area, concentration and the effect of using a catalyst. For each factor you must produce a table of data, a rate of reaction graph and a graph showing the effect of each factor on the rate of reaction. It is suggested that you use Excel to compile your data and draw your graphs.

PRACTICAL — INVESTIGATING THE RATE OF A REACTION

Design, plan and carry out an experiment to investigate the effect of one factor on the rate of a reaction. Your teacher will give you a series of suitable reactions and choice of factors for you to choose from. You will need to work with a partner. Use the following checklist to perform your investigation:

● Choose which reaction and factor you are going to investigate. Write an 'Introduction' to the investigation including: a word equation and balanced symbol equation of the reaction; a statement of what you expect to happen (with scientific reasoning); a diagram of your experiment; and a list of the apparatus you will use.
● Design a suitable practical experimental set-up to investigate your reaction and factor safely.
● Compile a suitable list of equipment and liaise with your teacher and science technician to order the equipment.
● Design a suitable data-recording table to collect and record your measurements.
● Produce a written 'Procedure' for your experiment.
● Use a supplied risk assessment template and relevant CLEAPSS guidance to produce a risk assessment for your experiment and make sure this is checked and approved by your teacher **before** attempting the experimental work.
● Assemble your apparatus and perform your experiment, working carefully and safely to measure and record any relevant experimental data.

continued...

PRACTICAL *contd.*

- If you are able to (your teacher will tell you if you have enough time), repeat your measurements, or liaise with another group to compile a series of repeated measurements (ensuring that the repeats are 'fair tests'). Use your repeats to determine mean values.
- Draw rate of reaction graphs and use them to measure the fastest rate of reaction for each value of the independent variable that you are investigating.
- Draw a graph of rate of reaction against the variable factor that you are investigating.
- Write an analysis of the rate of reaction versus variable factor graph:
  - State the shape/trend/pattern in the graph.
  - Use the shape/trend/pattern to determine the relationship between the rate of reaction and the variable factor that you have investigated.
  - What conclusion do you draw from your results?
- Write an evaluation of your experiment by thinking about:
  - The experimental method and ways it could be improved.
  - The quality of the data that you collected and how the quality could be improved.
  - To what extent does your data support your conclusion? (How certain are you about your conclusion considering the data that you collected?)
- Collate your report and submit it for assessment by your teacher. It should include:
  - introduction
  - risk assessment
  - table(s) of data
  - graphs
  - written analysis
  - written evaluation.

Chemical calculations

The Periodic Table arranges elements in order of their atomic number. The table also shows the masses of each element. The masses of individual atoms are incredibly small (an atom of hydrogen has a mass of 1.7×10^{-27} kg), so it is much more convenient to state the masses of the various atoms relative to each other. The relative atomic mass (A_r) of an element is the mass of an atom of that element compared with the mass of an atom of carbon-12. This atom of carbon is given the value of exactly 12. On the Periodic Table in Figure 11.17, the relative atomic mass is shown as the top number in each box and the bottom number is the atomic number of the element, as shown in Figure 11.16.

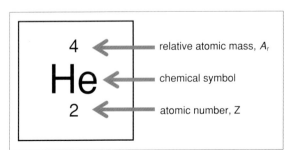

Figure 11.16 The position of the relative atomic mass and the atomic number for each element.

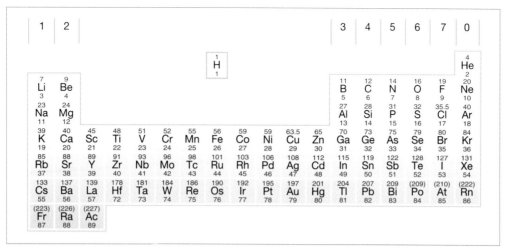

Figure 11.17 Periodic Table.

Knowing the relative atomic masses of the elements allows us to work out the **relative molecular masses (M_r)** of any compounds that contain those elements.

- **Water (H_2O)**: In this molecule, there are two hydrogen atoms and one oxygen atom. The relative molecular mass is $[(2 \times 1) + 16] = 18$.
- **Carbon dioxide (CO_2)**: In this molecule, there are two oxygen atoms and one carbon atom. The relative molecular mass is $[12 + (2 \times 16)] = 44$.

For ionic compounds like sodium chloride, it is more correct to use the term **relative formula mass**, as there are no separate molecules in ionic compounds.

- **Sodium chloride (NaCl)**: In this compound, there is one sodium ion for every one chloride ion. The relative formula mass is $[23 + 35.5] = 58.5$.
- **Sodium carbonate (Na_2CO_3)**: In this compound, there are two sodium ions, and one carbonate ion made up of one carbon and three oxygen atoms. The relative formula mass is $[(2 \times 23) + 12 + (3 \times 16)] = [46 + 12 + 48] = 106$.

Calculating percentage composition of compounds

The relative atomic mass of carbon is 12 and that of oxygen is 16. The relative molecular mass of carbon dioxide (CO_2) is 44. The percentage composition (by mass) of carbon and oxygen in carbon dioxide is calculated by:

$$\text{percentage of } \textbf{carbon} \text{ in } CO_2 = \frac{\text{total relative mass of } \textbf{carbon} \text{ in molecule}}{\text{relative molecular mass of carbon dioxide}} \times 100\%$$

$$= \frac{12}{44} \times 100 = 27.3\%$$

$$\text{percentage of } \textbf{oxygen} \text{ in } CO_2 = \frac{\text{total relative mass of } \textbf{oxygen} \text{ in molecule}}{\text{relative molecular mass of carbon dioxide}} \times 100\%$$

$$= \frac{32}{44} \times 100 = 72.7\%$$

Example

Q Calculate the percentage composition by mass of lithium sulfate, Li_2SO_4.

A Relative atomic masses: Li = 7; S = 32; O = 16

Relative formula mass of $Li_2SO_4 = (2 \times 7) + 32 + (4 \times 16) = 110$

$$\% \text{ composition of Li} = \frac{14}{110} \times 100 = 12.7\%$$

$$\% \text{ composition of S} = \frac{32}{110} \times 100 = 29.1\%$$

$$\% \text{ composition of O} = \frac{64}{110} \times 100 = 58.2\%$$

QUESTIONS

Use the Periodic Table, Figure 11.17, to help you with these questions.

10 Calculate the relative molecular mass, M_r, for the following molecules.

  a oxygen gas, O_2

  b sulfur dioxide, SO_2

  c methane, CH_4

  d nitrogen dioxide, NO_2

  e carbon tetrachloride, CCl_4

  f ammonia, NH_3

  g ethane, C_2H_6

11 Calculate the relative formula mass of the following ionic compounds.

  a lithium chloride, LiCl

  b potassium oxide, K_2O

  c sodium sulfide, Na_2S

  d magnesium carbonate, $MgCO_3$

  e calcium nitrate, $Ca(NO_3)_2$

  f beryllium oxide, BeO

  g rubidium carbonate, Rb_2CO_3

  h ammonium sulfate, $(NH_4)_2SO_4$

12 Calculate the percentage composition of each molecule or compound in Questions 10 and 11.

Calculating masses of reactants and products

Relative molecular and formula masses can be used to calculate the masses of reactants and products in a chemical reaction. The reaction of magnesium carbonate with hydrochloric acid is:

magnesium carbonate + hydrochloric acid → magnesium chloride + water + carbon dioxide

$$MgCO_3(s) \quad + \quad 2HCl(aq) \quad \rightarrow \quad MgCl_2(aq) \quad + \quad H_2O(l) \quad + \quad CO_2(g)$$

Total mass of reactants

mass of $MgCO_3$ + 2 × (mass of HCl) =
$(24 + 12 + (3 \times 16)) + 2 \times (1 + 35.5) = 157$

Total mass of products

mass of $MgCl_2$ + mass of H_2O + mass of CO_2 =
$(24 + (2 \times 35.5)) + ((2 \times 1) + 16) + (12 + (2 \times 16)) = 157$

Note that the total mass of the products is equal to the total mass of the reactants because no atoms are created or destroyed during a chemical reaction.

QUESTION

13 Calculate the total mass of reactants and products in the following reactions:
 a $N_2(g) + 3H_2(g) \rightarrow 2NH_3(g)$
 b $2H_2(g) + O_2(g) \rightarrow 2H_2O(g)$
 c $Mg(s) + H_2SO_4(aq) \rightarrow MgSO_4(aq) + H_2(g)$
 d $NaOH(aq) + HNO_3(aq) \rightarrow NaNO_3(aq) + H_2O(l)$

Using equations to calculate mass of products in a reaction

A balanced equation is a shorthand way of summarising a chemical reaction. The balanced equation can be used to predict the relationships between the masses of reacting compounds and the products they form.

Examples

Q Find the mass of carbon dioxide formed when 5.3 g of sodium carbonate completely reacts with excess hydrochloric acid.

$Na_2CO_3(s) + 2HCl(aq) \rightarrow 2NaCl(aq) + H_2O(l) + CO_2(g)$

A The relative formula mass of sodium carbonate is 106.
The relative molecular mass of carbon dioxide is 44.

Having selected the compounds we are interested in, we use the molecular or formula masses to write the following statements:

■ 106 g of sodium carbonate forms 44 g of carbon dioxide.
■ 1 g of sodium carbonate forms $\frac{44}{106}$ g of carbon dioxide.
■ 5.3 g of sodium carbonate forms $\left(\frac{44}{106} \times 5.3\right)$ g of carbon dioxide.

The mass of carbon dioxide formed is 2.2 g.

Q Calculate the mass of carbon monoxide needed to completely reduce 1000 g of iron(III) oxide inside a blast furnace.

$$Fe_2O_3(s) + 3CO(g) \rightarrow 2Fe(l) + 3CO_2(g)$$

A The relative formula mass of iron(III) oxide is 160.

The relative molecular mass of carbon monoxide is 28.

- 160 g of iron(III) oxide is reduced by ($3 \times 28 = 84$) g of carbon monoxide.
- 1 g of iron(III) oxide is reduced by $\frac{84}{160}$ g of carbon monoxide.
- 1000 g of iron(III) oxide is reduced by $\left(\frac{84}{160} \times 1000\right)$ g = 525 g of carbon monoxide.

QUESTIONS

14 Calculate the mass of calcium oxide formed by the complete decomposition of 5 kg of calcium carbonate.
$$CaCO_3(s) \rightarrow CaO(s) + CO_2(g)$$

15 Calculate the mass of sodium chloride that can be formed from the neutralisation of 8 g of sodium hydroxide with hydrochloric acid.
$$NaOH(aq) + HCl(aq) \rightarrow NaCl(aq) + H_2O(l)$$

16 Calculate the mass of calcium chloride that can be formed by the reaction of 3 g of calcium carbonate with an excess of hydrochloric acid.
$$CaCO_3(s) + 2HCl(aq) \rightarrow CaCl_2(aq) + H_2O(l) + CO_2(g)$$

PRACTICAL   CALCULATING THE FORMULA OF COPPER(II) OXIDE

This activity helps you with:
★ working as a team
★ taking careful scientific measurements
★ calculating the formula of simple compounds.

If you heat copper(II) oxide in a glass tube while passing methane over it, the copper(II) oxide reacts with the methane to produce copper, water and carbon dioxide. If the reactants and products are weighed carefully the formula of the copper(II) oxide can be deduced.

 Risk assessment

Your teacher will provide you with a risk assessment for this experiment.

Procedure
1 Weigh the reduction tube with the delivery tube bung in. Record this as **mass 1**.
2 Put two spatulas of copper(II) oxide into the tube and spread it out as evenly as possible along the length of the reduction tube.
3 Weigh the tube again, with the copper(II) oxide in it. Record this as **mass 2**.
4 Set up the apparatus as shown in Figure 11.18, but do not place the Bunsen burner underneath yet. Make sure that you clamp the reduction tube as near to the bung as possible.
5 Turn on the gas tap attached to the reduction tube. Adjust the gas flow to about halfway to get a steady flow of methane gas over the copper(II) oxide.

Apparatus
* copper(II) oxide
* reduction tube
* delivery tube bung to fit reduction tube
* rubber tubing
* stand, boss and clamp
* Bunsen burner
* heat resistant mat
* spatula
* electronic balance

PRACTICAL contd.

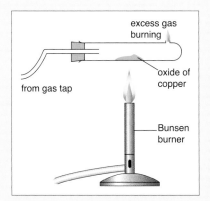

Figure 11.18 Heating copper(II) oxide with methane.

6 When all the air has flushed out of the tube, light the gas coming out of the exhaust hole at the end of the tube. Make sure that you do not lean over the tube as you light the gas. Adjust the gas tap so that the flame is about 3 cm high.

7 Light the Bunsen burner under the reduction tube and heat the copper oxide in the tube using a roaring flame. Pick up the base of the Bunsen burner and move the hottest part of the flame around underneath the copper(II) oxide to make sure that every bit of the copper(II) oxide is heated – this will take about 20 minutes.

8 If there are parts of the copper(II) oxide that look unreacted, gently shake the reduction tube using the clamp stand – **do not touch the hot reduction tube**.

9 When all the copper oxide has reacted (it will look like salmon-pink copper), keep heating for a minute and then turn off the Bunsen burner.

10 Keep passing the methane over the copper as it cools down to prevent it from reacting with any oxygen present and turning back into copper oxide (keep the exhaust flame burning). When the rest of the reduction tube is cool, switch off the gas supply.

11 Weigh the reduction tube with the delivery tube bung and the product. Record this as **mass 3**.

Analysing the results and calculating the formula of copper(II) oxide
1 Calculate the mass of **copper(II) oxide** reactant (**mass 2 – mass 1**).
2 Calculate the mass of **copper** product (**mass 3 – mass 1**).
3 Calculate the mass of **oxygen** in copper(II) oxide (**mass 2 – mass 3**).
The relative atomic mass of copper is 63.5 and oxygen is 16.
4 Calculate the relative ratio of copper in copper(II) oxide:

$$= \frac{\text{mass of copper}}{\text{relative atomic mass of copper}}$$

5 Calculate the relative ratio of oxygen in copper(II) oxide:

$$= \frac{\text{mass of oxygen}}{\text{relative atomic mass of oxygen}}$$

Compare the two relative ratios, divide the biggest ratio by the smallest ratio and this will tell you the proportion of copper atoms to oxygen atoms in copper(II) oxide.

If the proportion is 1:1 then the formula is CuO; if the proportion is 2:1 then the formula is Cu_2O; and if it is 1:2 then the formula is CuO_2 and so on.

PRACTICAL   CALCULATING THE FORMULA OF MAGNESIUM OXIDE

This activity helps you with:
★ working as a team
★ taking careful scientific measurements
★ calculating the formulae of simple compounds.

When magnesium is heated in air, it reacts with the oxygen. During this oxidation reaction, the grey compound magnesium oxide is produced. This increases the overall mass. Knowing the mass of the magnesium at the start, and the mass of magnesium oxide product, it is possible to work out the mass of oxygen which has reacted with the magnesium. These masses can be used to work out the formula of magnesium oxide.

continued...

Apparatus

* magnesium ribbon (approx. 10 cm)
* small piece of sandpaper
* heat resistant mat
* tripod
* Bunsen burner
* pipe-clay triangle
* crucible and lid
* tongs
* electronic balance

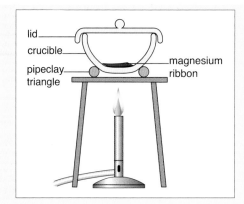

Figure 11.19 Set-up for burning magnesium in air.

 Risk assessment

Your teacher will give you a risk assessment for this experiment.

Procedure

1 Weigh the empty crucible with its lid using the electronic balance. Record this as **mass 1**.
2 Use the sandpaper to clean the piece of magnesium ribbon and then coil it around a pencil.
3 Place the magnesium ribbon coil into the crucible and put the lid on.
4 Weigh the crucible, lid and magnesium together. Record this as **mass 2**.
5 Place the crucible, lid and magnesium onto a pipe-clay triangle on top of a tripod. Make sure that the lid is slightly mis-fitting allowing air into the crucible.
6 Heat the crucible from below until the reaction has finished (the magnesium will glow at first, then turn to a grey coil).
7 Turn off the Bunsen burner and allow the crucible to cool.
8 Weigh the crucible with its lid and all its contents. Record this as **mass 3**.

Analysing the results and calculating the formula of magnesium oxide

1 Calculate the mass of **magnesium** reactant (**mass 2 – mass 1**).
2 Calculate the mass of **magnesium oxide** product (**mass 3 – mass 1**).
3 Calculate the mass of **oxygen** in magnesium oxide (**mass 3 – mass 2**).
The relative atomic mass of magnesium is 24 and oxygen is 16.
4 Calculate the relative ratio of magnesium in magnesium oxide:

$$= \frac{\text{mass of magnesium}}{\text{relative atomic mass of magnesium}}$$

5 Calculate the relative ratio of oxygen in magnesium oxide:

$$= \frac{\text{mass of oxygen}}{\text{relative atomic mass of oxygen}}$$

Compare the two relative ratios, divide the biggest ratio by the smallest ratio and this will tell you the proportion of magnesium atoms to oxygen atoms in magnesium oxide.

If the proportions are 1:1 then the formula is MgO; if the ratio is 2:1 then the formula is Mg_2O; and if it is 1:2 then the formula is MgO_2 and so on.

Calculating the yield of a chemical reaction

The reaction of magnesium with oxygen used in the Practical **Calculating the formula of magnesium oxide** produces magnesium oxide. The chemical equations for this reaction are:

$$\text{magnesium} + \text{oxygen} \rightarrow \text{magnesium oxide}$$
$$2Mg(s) + O_2(g) \rightarrow 2MgO(s)$$

The relative atomic mass of magnesium is 24 and oxygen is 16. This means that the relative formula mass of magnesium oxide is 40. The equation tells us that (2×24) g of magnesium produces (2×40) g of magnesium oxide. So:

48 g of magnesium makes 80 g of magnesium oxide

1 g of magnesium makes $\dfrac{80}{48}$ = 1.7 g of magnesium oxide

Therefore, in an experiment using 5 g of magnesium you would expect to get (5×1.7) = 8.5 g of magnesium oxide. This is the **theoretical yield** of the reaction.

If only 7.9 g of magnesium oxide is produced, this is called the **actual yield** of the reaction.

The percentage yield of the reaction is calculated by:

$$\text{percentage yield} = \frac{\text{actual yield}}{\text{theoretical yield}} \times 100\%$$

So for this reaction:

$$\text{percentage yield} = \frac{7.9}{8.5} \times 100\% = 92.9\%$$

QUESTIONS

17 Calculate the percentage yield for the Practical **Calculating the formula of magnesium oxide** (pages 125–6).

18 Six tonnes of ethanol is produced from 15 tonnes of ethene when it is reacted with an excess of water. Calculate the percentage yield of the reaction.
$$C_2H_4(g) + H_2O(g) \rightarrow C_2H_5OH(g)$$

19 Find the percentage yield of the reaction if 5 g of CO_2 is released from the decomposition of 10 g of $CaCO_3$.
$$CaCO_3(s) \rightarrow CaO(s) + CO_2(g)$$

Calculating energy changes

When chemical reactions occur, new substances (the products) are formed from the reacting substances (the reactants). Combustion is a particular type of reaction involving a fuel burning in oxygen. In the case of the complete combustion of hydrocarbons, such as methane, the reactants are the hydrocarbon and oxygen, and the products are carbon dioxide and water. The combustion reaction involves breaking bonds in the reactants and reforming bonds to form the products. A hydrocarbon molecule contains only carbon and hydrogen atoms and during the reaction, those atoms form bonds with oxygen atoms.

Consider the combustion of methane (see Figure 11.20):

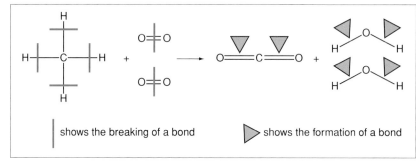

shows the breaking of a bond ▽ shows the formation of a bond

Figure 11.20 Combustion of methane involves the breaking and reforming of bonds.

$$\begin{array}{cccc} \text{methane} & + \ \text{oxygen} & \rightarrow & \text{carbon dioxide} & + & \text{water} \\ CH_4(g) & + \ 2O_2(g) & \rightarrow & CO_2(g) & + & 2H_2O(g) \end{array}$$

The **breaking** of a bond is **endothermic**. This means it requires **energy to be put in**. The **formation** of a bond is **exothermic** – **it gives out energy**. The difference between the total energy needed to break all the bonds and the total energy given out when the new bonds are formed determines whether the overall reaction is exothermic or endothermic.

Bond energy data

The table below shows the energy values for some covalent bonds.

Table 11.1 Energy values for covalent bonds

Bond	Bond energy (kJ)
O=O	496
C–H	412
H–H	436
C=O	743
O–H	463
C–C	348
N≡N	944
C=C	612
N–H	388

For bonds to be broken the amount of energy equivalent to the bond energy needs to be put in, and when bonds are formed, the amount of energy equivalent to the bond energy is given out.

Example

The complete combustion of methane is given by:

$$CH_4(g) + 2O_2(g) \rightarrow CO_2(g) + 2H_2O(g)$$

The bonds broken are four C–H bonds and two O=O bonds (Figure 11.23), so the total energy put in is:

$4 \times C\text{–}H = (4 \times 412) = 1648\,kJ$

$2 \times O\text{=}O = (2 \times 496) = 992\,kJ$

total energy in = 2640 kJ

The bonds formed are two C=O bonds and four O–H bonds:

$2 \times C=O = (2 \times 743) = 1486\,kJ$

$4 \times O–H = (4 \times 463) = 1852\,kJ$

total energy out = 3338 kJ

The heat of combustion is total energy out – total energy in = 3338 – 2640 = 698 kJ.

In this example, as is the case with all fuels, more energy is given out than is taken in, and so the reaction is **exothermic** and gives out energy (the whole point of burning a fuel).

Exothermic reactions **give out heat** to the surroundings.
Endothermic reactions **take in heat** from the surroundings.

Example

Q Ammonia is made by the combination of nitrogen gas and hydrogen gas. As we saw earlier in the chapter it is called the Haber Process when it's carried out on an industrial scale. Find out if the reaction below is exothermic or endothermic.

$N_2(g) + 3H_2(g) \rightarrow 2NH_3(g)$

A The bonds broken are one N≡N bond and three H–H bonds. The energy taken in is:

$1 \times N≡N = 944\,kJ$

$3 \times H–H = (3 \times 436) = 1308\,kJ$

total energy in = 2252 kJ

The bonds formed are six N–H bonds, so the energy given out is:
$6 \times N–H = (6 \times 388) = 2328\,kJ$

total energy out = 2328 kJ

energy change = total energy out – total energy in
= 2328 – 2252 = **76 kJ**

More energy is given out when the ammonia forms than when the nitrogen and hydrogen molecules break. Therefore the reaction is exothermic.

QUESTIONS

Perform energy calculations to decide if the following reactions are exothermic or endothermic.

20 The combustion of ethanol: $C_2H_5OH(l) + 3O_2(g) \rightarrow 2CO_2(g) + 3H_2O(g)$.

21 The neutralisation of sodium hydroxide by hydrochloric acid:
$HCl(aq) + NaOH(aq) \rightarrow NaCl(aq) + H_2O(l)$.

22 The reaction of lithium with water: $2Li(s) + H_2O(l) \rightarrow 2LiOH(aq) + H_2(g)$.

23 The reaction of nitrogen and oxygen gas: $N_2(g) + O_2(g) \rightarrow 2NO(g)$.

Chapter summary

- Plan and carry out experiments to study the effect of any relevant factor on the rate of a chemical reaction, using appropriate technology e.g. a light sensor and data logger to follow the precipitation of sulfur during the reaction between sodium thiosulfate and hydrochloric acid.
- Analyse data collected in order to draw conclusions, and critically evaluate the method of data collection, the quality of the data and to what extent the data support the conclusion.
- Explore the particle theory explanation of rate changes, arising from changing concentration (pressure), temperature and particle size, using a range of sources including textbooks and computer simulations.
- A catalyst increases the rate of a chemical change while remaining chemically unchanged itself and reduces the energy required for a collision to be successful.
- There is great economic and environmental importance in developing new and better catalysts, in terms of increasing yields, preserving raw materials, reducing energy costs etc.
- The formula of a binary compound, e.g. magnesium oxide, can be calculated using collected experimental data or given data.
- The percentage composition of simple compounds can be calculated using the relative atomic masses of the elements and the relative formula mass of the molecule.
- The masses of reactants or products can be calculated from a balanced symbol equation for a reaction.
- The percentage yield of a reaction can be worked out.
- Endothermic reactions take in energy.
- Exothermic reactions give out energy.
- Given bond energy data can be used to calculate the overall energy change for a reaction and to identify whether it is exothermic or endothermic.

Organic chemistry

Organic chemistry is the chemistry of carbon-based compounds. It is particularly important because all life on the planet is carbon-based, and so many organic chemicals are necessary for life processes. Carbon-based compounds have a lot of industrial uses, too.

Why is oil so important?

The crude oil that is extracted from oil wells is a mixture of hydrocarbons, that is, organic chemicals containing only carbon and hydrogen. The chemicals were once part of living things, because oil is formed from a process of fossilisation. That is why oil is called a **fossil fuel**. Oil is vital to the world's economy, because so many useful products can be made from it via the process of fractional distillation, which you learnt about in the GCSE Science course.

Fractional distillation is a way of separating out different 'fractions' of the oil. The fractions still consist of a mixture of compounds, but with fewer chemicals than in the original oil, it is simpler to purify them.

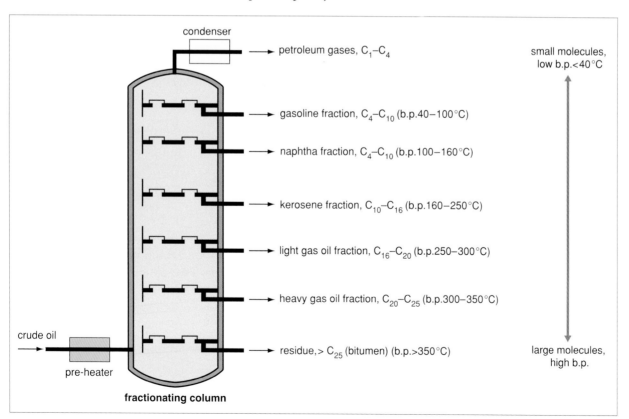

Figure 12.1 The fractional distillation of crude oil.

The different chemicals in crude oil have different boiling points. The boiling point is also the temperature at which the gas will condense into a liquid when it is cooled down. The oil is heated causing it to evaporate and turn into a gaseous mixture, and as the vapour rises in the fractional distillation column, it cools. At various points, the condensing liquid is extracted from the column, as shown in Figure 12.1. The larger the molecule is, the higher its boiling point will be, so the extracted molecules get smaller as you go up the column.

The chemicals in the different fractions are used to make a wide variety of useful products, including petrol, diesel, paraffin, methane, lubricating oil and bitumen. Oil products are also used to make plastics.

Alkanes and alkenes

Alkanes and alkenes are categories of hydrocarbon. Alkanes are **saturated** hydrocarbons. They contain single bonds only, and so they are 'saturated' with hydrogen (i.e. they contain as much hydrogen as possible). The difference between different alkanes is the number of carbon atoms they contain. The first four are shown in Table 12.1.

Table 12.1 Alkanes and their structure.

Name of alkane	Chemical/molecular formula	Structural formula
Methane	CH_4	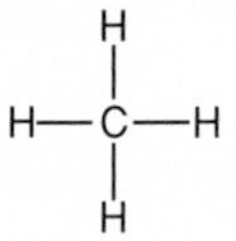
Ethane	C_2H_6	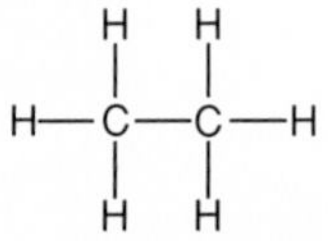
Propane	C_3H_8	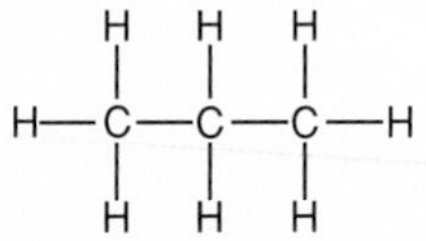
Butane	C_4H_{10}	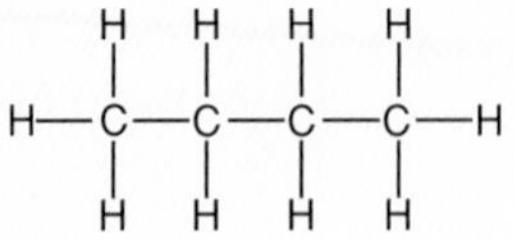

Alkenes are unsaturated hydrocarbons, which have at least one double bond between carbon atoms. Two alkenes are shown in Figure 12.2.

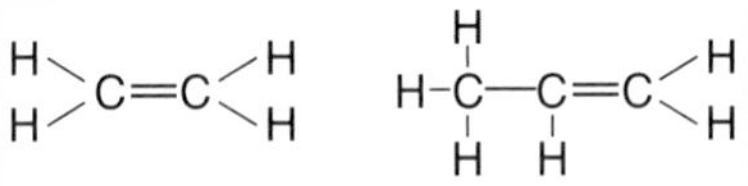

Figure 12.2 The structure of two alkenes.

Alkenes can be produced from alkanes by heating the alkane with a catalyst – a process known as **cracking**.

Addition reactions of alkenes

The presence of at least one carbon–carbon double bond in alkenes means that other atoms can be added to the molecule. Reactions that do this are called **addition reactions**, and two atoms that can be added in this way are hydrogen and bromine.

When hydrogen is added to an alkene (**hydrogenation**), the corresponding alkane is formed. This reaction is carried out by heating the alkene under pressure, in the presence of a metallic catalyst. The hydrogenation of ethene to form ethane is shown below.

$$C_2H_4 + H_2 \longrightarrow C_2H_6$$
$$\text{ethene} \quad \text{hydrogen} \quad \text{ethane}$$

Another addition reaction occurs with bromine to form a **dibromoalkane**. The double bond breaks and two bromine atoms attach.

This reaction is useful because it can be used to test for the presence of an alkene. Yellow bromine water reacts with the alkene and its colour disappears because the product formed is colourless.

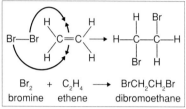

Figure 12.3 Addition reaction of ethene with bromine.

PRACTICAL   MAKING ALKENES FROM ALKANES

This activity helps you with:
★ following detailed instructions
★ handling apparatus.

In this activity paraffin (a mixture of alkanes) is heated using a catalyst to produce alkenes.

Risk assessment

Wear eye protection.
Your teacher will provide you with a risk assessment.

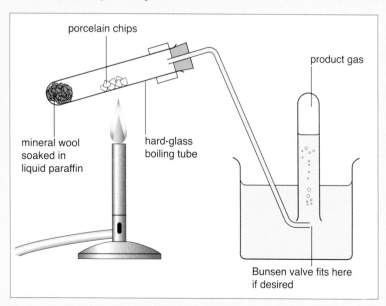

Figure 12.4 Experimental set up for making alkenes.

continued...

Apparatus (per group)
* 4 test tubes
* bungs, to fit test tubes
* test-tube rack
* boiling tube
* bung, one-holed, to fit boiling tube
* delivery tube fitted with a Bunsen valve
* small glass trough or plastic basin, for gas collection over water
* Bunsen burner
* heat resistant mat
* stand and clamp
* dropping pipette
* wooden splint
* about 2 cm³ medicinal paraffin (liquid paraffin – NOT the fuel)
* porous pot or pumice stone fragments
* about 2 cm³ bromine water, 0.02 mol dm⁻³, diluted to a pale yellow-orange colour,
* about 2 cm³ acidified potassium manganate(VII) solution, about 0.001 mol dm⁻³
* mineral wool (preferably 'Superwool')

Procedure

1 Place about a 2 cm depth of mineral wool in the bottom of the boiling tube and gently press it in place with a glass rod. Drop about 2 cm³ of liquid paraffin onto the wool, using a dropping pipette. Use enough paraffin to completely soak the mineral wool, but not so much that the paraffin runs along the side of the tube when it is placed horizontally.

2 Clamp the boiling tube near the mouth so that it is tilted slightly upwards, as shown in Figure 12.4. Place a heap of catalyst (pumice stone or porous pot fragments) in the centre of the tube and fit the delivery tube.

3 Fill the trough about two-thirds full with water and position the apparatus so that the end of the delivery tube is well immersed in the water.

4 Fill four test tubes with water and stand them inverted in the trough. Also place the test tube bungs, upside down, in the water.

5 Strongly heat the catalyst in the middle of the tube for a few minutes, until the glass is up to a dull red heat. Avoid heating the tube too close to the rubber bung.

6 While keeping the catalyst hot, flick the flame from time to time to the end of the tube for a few seconds to vaporise some of the liquid paraffin. Try to produce a steady stream of bubbles from the delivery tube. Be careful not to heat the liquid paraffin too strongly or let the catalyst cool down. To avoid suck-back do not remove the flame from heating the tube while gas is being collected. If suck-back looks as if it is about to occur, lift the whole apparatus by lifting the clamp stand.

7 When a steady stream of gas bubbles is established, collect four tubes full of gas by holding them over the Bunsen valve. Take care not to lift the water-filled tubes out of the water when moving them, to avoid letting air into them. Seal the full tubes by pressing them down on the bungs, then place them in a rack.

8 When gas collection is complete, first remove the delivery tube from the water by tilting or lifting the clamp stand. Only then stop heating.

9 Test the tubes of gas as follows:

  a Carefully smell the first test tube, and compare by smelling the liquid paraffin.

  b Use a lighted splint to see if the gas is flammable. The first tube may contain mostly air. If it does not ignite, try the second tube. Once the gas is lit, invert the test tube to allow the heavier-than-air gas to flow out and burn.

  c To the third tube of gas add 2−3 drops of bromine water, stopper and shake well.

  d To the fourth tube add 2−3 drops of acidified potassium manganate(VII) solution, stopper and shake well. This is another test for alkenes, the presence of which is indicated by a colour change to brown or colourless.

QUESTIONS

1 Look at the structural formula in Figure 12.5. Is this chemical an alkane or an alkene? Give a reason for your answer.

2 Alkenes are more reactive than alkanes. Suggest a reason for this, using your knowledge of their chemical structure.

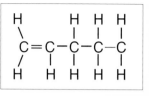

Figure 12.5

How can alkenes be made into polymers?

Alkene molecules can be assembled together in large numbers to make a variety of useful **polymers**, such as polythene, polypropene, polytetrafluoroethene (PTFE) and polyvinylchloride (PVC).

The small molecules (such as ethene) which are used to form polymers are called **monomers**. Polymers come in two types:

■ **addition polymers**, which are made from only one monomer
■ **condensation polymers**, which are made from two or more different monomers.

Ethene molecules can be assembled together to form the addition polymer poly(ethene), more commonly known as **polythene**. This is done by heating ethene under pressure. The number of molecules joining up varies, but is generally between 2000 and 20 000 (see Figure 12.6).

Polythene is commonly used for plastic carrier bags. It is flexible but not very strong.

Some other addition polymers are shown in Table 12.2.

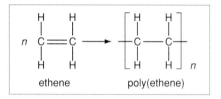

Figure 12.6 Formation of the addition polymer poly(ethene) from ethene (n is a variable large number).

Table 12.2 Addition polymers and their uses.

Name	Repeating unit	Uses
Polypropene	$\begin{bmatrix} & CH_3 & H \\ & \vert & \vert \\ - & C - C & - \\ & \vert & \vert \\ & H & H \end{bmatrix}_n$	Dishwasher-safe food containers; piping; automotive parts; waterproof carpets
Polyvinylchloride PVC	$\begin{bmatrix} & H & Cl \\ & \vert & \vert \\ - & C - C & - \\ & \vert & \vert \\ & H & H \end{bmatrix}_n$	Very widely used; pipes; window and door frames; clothing; electrical insulation
polytetrafluoroethene PTFE	$\begin{bmatrix} & F & F \\ & \vert & \vert \\ - & C - C & - \\ & \vert & \vert \\ & F & F \end{bmatrix}_n$	Known as Teflon; non-stick coating for cookware, irons, wiper blades etc.

What's the difference between a thermoplastic and a thermoset?

You may have noticed that some polymers, such as polythene, become soft when heated and go hard again when cooled. Other plastics, such as those used to make saucepan handles, are resistant to heat. Plastics that soften when heated are called thermo-softening plastics, or **thermoplastics**. Those plastics that are resistant to heat are called thermosetting plastics, or **thermosets**.

Thermoplastics are used extensively for household containers such as bowls and buckets, and for packaging material. Thermosets are used for electric light fittings, saucepan handles, and other products where heat resistance is important. The difference in the behaviour of these two types of polymer can be explained in terms of their structures. Thermoplastics are made up of polymer chains that are not linked together and so can slide over one another. This results in them being easy to melt. In thermosets, the polymer chains have strong cross linkages which hold the structure together and make them resistant to heat (see Figure 12.7).

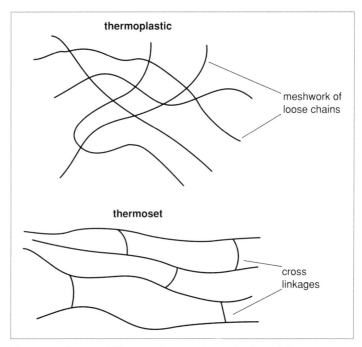

Figure 12.7 Structural differences between thermoplastics and thermosets.

Figure 12.8 Epoxy glue is a thermoset plastic. The chemical reaction between the resin and the hardeners cures the glue, which then sets. Once set, it is resistant to heat.

Thermoset plastics can be moulded. They usually start in a liquid form and they can be set by heat, chemical reactions or radiation. Once set, though, they cannot be re-melted.

TASK   WHY USE THIS PLASTIC?

This activity helps you with:
★ researching information on the internet
★ developing communication skills.

Find an item at home that is made of plastic. Look for a recycling mark on it (it will look something like Figure 12.9, but the number and lettering may be different).

1 Research on the internet to find out what plastic this item is made of, using the recycling sign.
2 Find out the properties of this plastic, and suggest why it is used for the item you have chosen.

Figure 12.9 Recycling sign on a plastic item.

Chapter summary

○ Fractional distillation of crude oil involves the heating and evaporation of the oil, followed by the condensation of different fractions at different temperatures as the vapour rises up the column.

○ Alkanes and alkenes are both examples of hydrocarbons. Alkanes are saturated and have no double bonds, but alkenes have at least one carbon-carbon double bond.

○ Ethene can undergo addition reactions with hydrogen and bromine. The reaction with bromine can be used as a test for alkenes.

○ Addition polymers are formed by the joining together of large numbers of molecules of a single monomer.

○ Thermoplastics melt easily but thermosets are heat resistant. This is due to their different structures.

13 Water

Water is a very important chemical. It is essential to life on our planet, and the human body (and those of other animals and plants) is mostly water. In the chemical industries, water is an important raw material that is used as:

- a solvent – solutions of compounds in water occur in many processes.
- a coolant – many chemical reactions produce heat that must be taken away from the plant; water cools processes, and then the water is itself cooled before being returned to the environment.

In this chapter we will look at issues around the supply and use of water in our homes, and some of its uses as a solvent.

How do we get clean water?

In Britain, almost everybody gets water piped into their homes, and this water is fit to drink straight from the tap. The water originates mainly as rainfall, but it has to be cleaned and treated before it is safe to drink. The rainfall is collected in lakes or man-made reservoirs where it is stored. Alternative water supplies are rivers and underground water. The Caban Coch dam in the Elan valley is shown in Figure 13.1; water from the Elan valley is used by the city of Birmingham in England. There are around 2000 such reservoirs supplying drinking water in the UK.

Figure 13.1 The Caban Coch dam in the Elan Valley in Powys.

The water coming from a reservoir will contain a lot of suspended particles and bacteria. These have to be removed to make the water palatable and safe to drink. This happens in water treatment plants, and the main stages are shown in Figure 13.2.

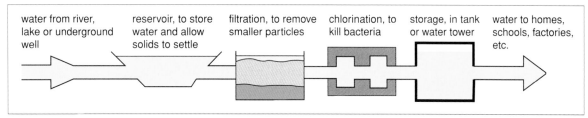

| water from river, lake or underground well | reservoir, to store water and allow solids to settle | filtration, to remove smaller particles | chlorination, to kill bacteria | storage, in tank or water tower | water to homes, schools, factories, etc. |

Figure 13.2 Stages in the treatment of drinking water.

QUESTIONS

1 In areas of the world where the drinking water is not fully treated, or when the water is thought to have been contaminated, people are asked to boil the water for several minutes and then cool it before drinking it. Suggest the reason for this.

2 Suggest five ways in which an average home could reduce the amount of water used per day.

Discussion Point

The water on the planet is constantly recycled by the water cycle, so why do we need to conserve water, if what we use eventually finds its way back to rivers and reservoirs?

While the water is in the reservoir, the larger solid particles will settle to the bottom (**sedimentation**). When the water is extracted from the reservoir, it is filtered to remove smaller particles (**filtration**), but these filters cannot remove bacteria. To kill the bacteria, the water is **chlorinated** (chlorine is added), and in some places fluoride is added to the water as a public health measure, as it is thought to help prevent tooth decay, particularly in young children. The treated water is then stored in a water tower or tank until it is needed.

Do we need to be careful about how much water we use?

It has been estimated that each person in the UK uses about 150 litres of water a day, for drinking, washing, cleaning and flushing. This is just domestic use and does not take into account water used by businesses and factories. In dry summers, reservoirs can run so low that local authorities have had to ban people from watering their gardens and washing their cars.

Figure 13.3 Water conservation poster.

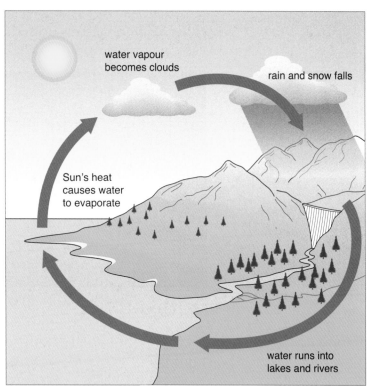

Figure 13.4 The water cycle.

Can we get drinking water from the sea?

Although the UK is surrounded by sea, we cannot drink sea water. The salt in it makes it taste unpleasant, but it also means that, if you did drink it, it would actually dehydrate you.

However, in various parts of the world, some countries are looking at the possibility of removing the salt from sea water (**desalination**) so that it can be used for drinking. The first desalination plant in the UK opened in 2010.

The usual process for desalination is called reverse osmosis. The sea water is filtered under pressure through a membrane which acts like a molecular filter, letting only the small water molecules go through, and keeping the salt back.

There are a number of problems with using desalination for supplying drinking water:

- The process uses a lot of energy because of the need to generate high pressures – much more than other processes that are used to produce drinking water.
- The process is expensive because of the energy needed.
- The desalination plants produce greenhouse gases, whereas normal water treatment plants produce very little.
- The very salty water left when the fresh water has been extracted is a pollutant and needs to be disposed of carefully.
- Some countries with a drought problem are very poor and could not afford desalination, while others are not on a coast, so the water would have to be piped long distances.

Desalination is extensively used in the Middle East, where rainfall is very low and the states tend to be wealthy. Many countries there have coastlines, and many produce oil meaning that their energy costs are not so high.

Figure 13.5 The first desalination plant in the UK, which opened near London in 2010.

How can you purify water when it is mixed with other liquids?

During the treatment of water for drinking, solid particles are separated by filtration. If something is dissolved in water, we can extract the water by evaporating it and then condensing the vapour, leaving the solute behind. But what if the water is mixed with another liquid? This requires a different technique (which has already been mentioned in connection with crude oil in Chapter 12) – **distillation**.

Each chemical has its own boiling point, and for water this is 100 °C. If you heat a mixture of liquids to 100 °C, then any vapour coming off at that point is water. Other liquids will boil off at lower or higher temperatures.

PRACTICAL   SEPARATING ETHANOL AND WATER

This practical may be done as a class experiment, or your teacher may show you a demonstration.

This activity helps you with:
★ evaluating experimental methods
★ developing communication skills.

 Risk assessment

Your teacher will provide a risk assessment for this experiment.

Procedure
1 Set up the apparatus as shown in Figure 13.6.
2 Gently heat the distillation flask, keeping an eye on the thermometer.
3 The boiling point of ethanol is 78 °C. When this temperature is reached, ethanol vapour should start to reach the condenser where it will be cooled and therefore form the liquid. Keep the temperature as close as possible to 78 °C by removing and replacing the Bunsen as necessary.
4 Continue until the distillate stops dripping from the condenser.
5 When the distillation flask has cooled, compare the smell of the liquids in the distillation flask and the conical flask.

Apparatus
* clamp stand × 2
* gauze
* Bunsen burner
* distillation flask
* thermometer
* condenser
* conical flask
* ethanol/water mixture

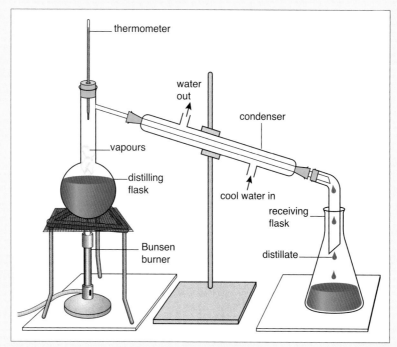

Figure 13.6 Experimental set-up for simple distillation.

Evaluating your experiment
Evaluate this method of separating ethanol and water. Are there any improvements that could be made to the experimental method?

This simple distillation procedure is fine for separating two liquids with clearly different boiling points. For mixtures of several different liquids, a fractionating column is used (see Figure 13.7). The increased surface area of the fractionating column encourages the liquids to condense, in particular those with higher boiling points.

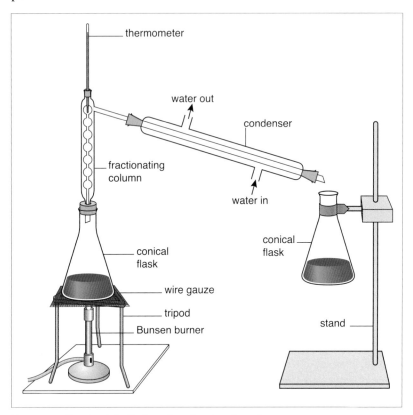

Figure 13.7 Fractional distillation using a fractionating column.

How can we identify substances in a solution?

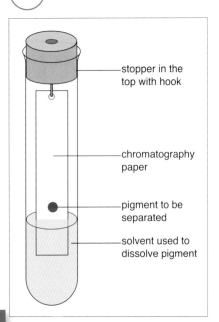

Figure 13.8 Paper chromatography.

Sometimes, we want to identify and separate substances in a mixed solution. Distillation is no good here because there is only one solvent. Instead, we can use **chromatography**. In paper chromatography, a drop of the mixture is placed on chromatography paper and the paper is then placed in a container of solvent, with the level of the solvent just below the level of the spot (see Figure 13.8).

The solvent soaks into the paper and moves upwards. Any soluble substance in the pigment dissolves in the solvent and travels up the paper with it. The most soluble substances travel as far as the solvent does, but less soluble substances 'trail behind'. As a result, the different substances can be seen on the paper (if they are coloured – see Figure 13.9).

The substances can be identified by how far they have travelled. To measure this, scientists calculate something called an R_f value. Figure 13.10 shows how this is calculated.

Figure 13.9 Results of paper chromatography on different dyes.

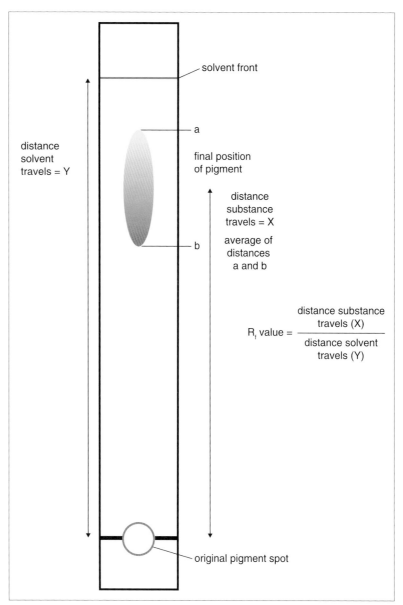

solvent front

distance solvent travels = Y

a

final position of pigment

distance substance travels = X

b

average of distances a and b

$$R_f \text{ value} = \frac{\text{distance substance travels (X)}}{\text{distance solvent travels (Y)}}$$

original pigment spot

Figure 13.10 Calculation of R_f value.

As the spot is usually spread out, the distance travelled is calculated by averaging the maximum and minimum distances travelled.

The R_f value of a substance is different for different solvents. It is possible for two different substances to have the same R_f value in a certain solvent, but they would not have identical R_f values in several different solvents, so sometimes chromatography has to be done in different solvents to conclusively identify a solute.

Apparatus
* 250 cm³ beaker
* chromatography paper
* dropping pipette
* ink samples A–D
* results of chromatography on ink from the suicide note

Mr Davies has been found dead, and seems to have left a suicide note. However, the police suspect he may have been murdered and the murderer may have forged the note. Chromatography has been done on the ink of the note, and you are provided with the results. You are also provided with samples of ink from Mr Davies' pen and the pens of the three main suspects.

INK SAMPLE A comes from Mr Davies' pen.
INK SAMPLE B comes from the pen of Mr Davies' wife, Emily.
INK SAMPLE C comes from the pen of Jack Lee, who is thought to be having an affair with Emily Davies.
INK SAMPLE D comes from the pen of Tom Kelly, a business rival of Mr Davies.
Analyse the ink samples using chromatography, and decide:
Was Mr Davies murdered, and if so, by who?

 Risk assessment

There are no significant risks in this experiment.

Procedure
1 Calculate the R_f values of the ink pigments from the suicide note.
2 Set up the apparatus as shown in Figure 13.11.

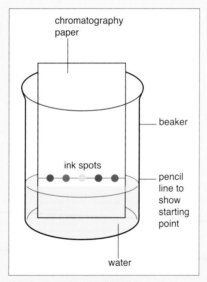

chromatography paper

beaker

ink spots

pencil line to show starting point

water

Figure 13.11 Experimental set-up of chromatography experiment.

3 Leave until water has soaked up nearly to the top of the paper.
4 Remove the paper and mark how far the water has reached (the 'solvent front').
5 Calculate the R_f value of each coloured pigment in each ink. Record your results in a table.
6 Use the evidence to suggest who killed Mr Davies. Justify your conclusions, and explain the strength of the evidence.

WATER

What is gas chromatography?

Another form of chromatography is gas chromatography. This is an analytical technique used by chemists to detect and measure small amounts of certain chemicals present in a mixture. It can be used to detect pollutants in water or in air, and is also a technique used by authorities to test for banned substances in the blood of sports players.

In gas chromatography, the mixture must be in the form of a gas, either naturally, or by the heating and vaporisation of a liquid. The gas passes through a column and the different substances are absorbed onto an inert solid or liquid inside the column. The distance the substances travel along the column is determined by their chemical and physical properties. Their position in the column is detected electronically.

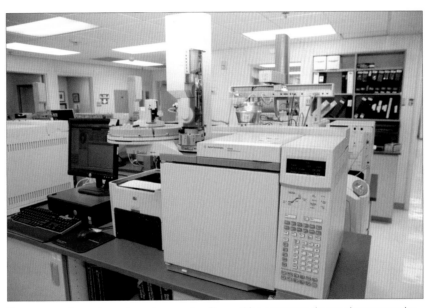

Figure 13.12 A gas chromatograph apparatus. The machine automates the gas chromatography procedure, and gives a direct read-out of results.

TASK

HOW IS SOLUBILITY AFFECTED BY TEMPERATURE?

This activity helps you with:
★ reading data from a graph
★ interpreting graphical data
★ developing communication skills.

Water has been described as the 'universal solvent'. A wide variety of substances dissolve in it, to different extents. A chemical which dissolves in a solvent is called a **solute**. For each solute, there is a limit to how much can dissolve in a solvent. When no more can dissolve, the solution is said to be **saturated**, although under certain circumstances it is possible to increase the amount of solute, giving a **supersaturated** solution.

Figure 13.13 shows the effect of temperature on the solubility of some sodium and potassium compounds. Such graphs are called **solubility curves**.

continued...

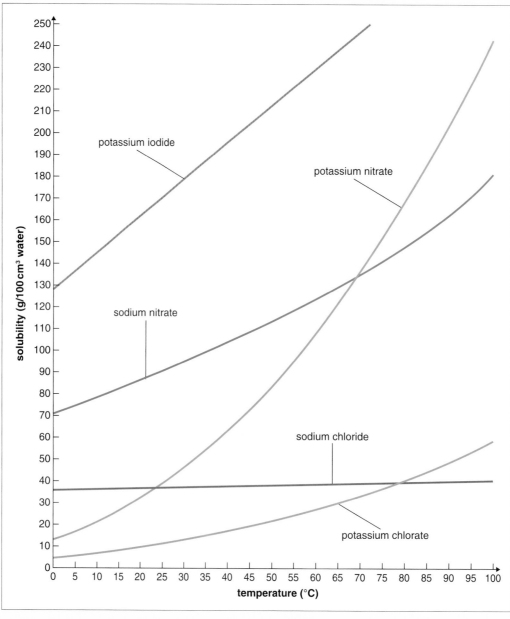

Figure 13.13 Solubility curves for some potassium and sodium compounds.

1 How much sodium nitrate can dissolve in water at 30 °C?
2 Which compound is the least soluble at 50 °C?
3 Which compound's solubility is least affected by temperature?
4 How much extra potassium iodide can dissolve in 100 cm³ of water if the temperature is increased from 15 °C to 30 °C?
5 Are the following solutions unsaturated, saturated or supersaturated?
   a 40 g/100 cm³ sodium chloride at 75 °C
   b 2 g/100 cm³ potassium chlorate at 45 °C
   c 155 g/100 cm³ potassium iodide at 15 °C
   d 100 g/100 cm³ sodium nitrate at 30 °C
6 Compare the solubility curves for potassium iodide and potassium nitrate.

What makes water hard or soft?

The water that comes out of your tap may be 'hard' or 'soft' depending on what area of the country you live in and where your water comes from. Hard water is water that contains dissolved calcium (Ca^{2+}) and magnesium (Mg^{2+}) ions.

Hard water can be **temporary** or **permanent**, or a mixture of the two. Temporary hard water contains calcium hydrogencarbonate and/or magnesium hydrogencarbonate. When this water is heated, the hardness is removed, with the formation of calcium carbonate.

$$Ca(HCO_3)_2(aq) \rightarrow CaCO_3(s) + H_2O(l) + CO_2(g)$$

This can cause a problem in boilers, hot water tanks and cooling systems, because the calcium carbonate formed clogs up the pipes and restricts flow (see Figure 13.14). Similar deposits will also build up in domestic appliances such as kettles, washing machines and dishwashers in hard water areas.

Permanent hard water contains chlorides and/or sulfates of calcium and magnesium, and heating does not soften this water. Of course, it is possible for water to contain a variety of calcium and magnesium compounds, and so its hardness may be a mixture of temporary and permanent. In such cases, heating will remove some of the hardness, but not all.

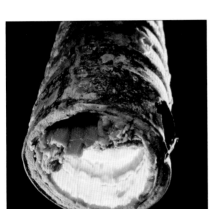

Figure 13.14 The effect of hard water on a heating pipe.

PRACTICAL — HOW CAN WE TELL THE DIFFERENCE BETWEEN HARD AND SOFT WATER?

Soft water lathers easily with soap but hard water does not. Soap reacts with hard water to form the calcium or magnesium salt of the organic acid in the soap. These salts are insoluble and form greyish soap scum, but no lather. We can therefore test the hardness of water by seeing how well it lathers when soap is added. Remember that temporary hardness can be removed by boiling but permanent hardness cannot.

This activity helps you with:
★ presenting results in tables and graphs
★ interpreting results
★ evaluating experimental methods.

 Risk assessment

Wear eye protection.
Your teacher will provide a risk assessment for this experiment.

Apparatus
* conical flask and stopper
* burette
* 100 cm³ measuring cylinder
* water samples, labelled A, B, C and D
* boiled samples of A, B, C and D
* stop watch
* soap solution

continued...

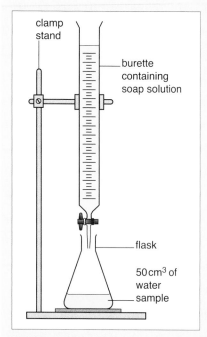

Figure 13.15 Experimental set-up to test water for hardness.

Procedure

1 Measure 50 cm³ of water sample A into a conical flask.
2 Using the burette, add 1 cm³ of soap solution, insert the stopper and shake vigorously for 5 seconds.
3 Repeat step 2 until a lather forms that lasts for 30 seconds.
4 Record the total volume of soap solution added.
5 Repeat steps 2–4 with 50 cm³ of the boiled sample of A.
6 Repeat steps 1–5 with water samples B, C and D.
7 Record all your results in a table.
8 Draw a bar graph of the results.

Analysing your results

1 Use your results to describe the hardness of each water sample, and whether this hardness is temporary or permanent. Explain the reasons for your identification.
2 This method works fairly successfully for *comparing* the hardness of the water samples. Suggest an improvement that could be made if you wanted a more accurate *measure* of water hardness.

How can we soften hard water?

There are three main ways of softening water, each with their own advantages and disadvantages.

1 Boiling

Boiling removes hardness and is easy and cheap, but it is only practical for small quantities of water, and it also causes deposits on the water container. It cannot remove permanent hardness.

2 Adding sodium carbonate

Sodium carbonate can be purchased as washing soda and is added to washing machine loads to soften the water. It prevents the calcium and magnesium ions bonding to the washing detergent, meaning that less detergent has to be used. It is cheap and can remove permanent hardness, but deposits are still formed.

3 Ion exchange columns

An ion exchange column is a tube filled with a resin. Water is passed through the column and sodium ions on the resin exchange with the calcium and magnesium ions, so removing them from the water and softening it. Eventually the resin has to be 'regenerated' by passing concentrated sodium chloride through it to replace the lost sodium. Water softeners are quite expensive but can treat a large amount of water, and can remove both temporary and permanent hardness. The waste from the regeneration process in industrial-scale water softening plants can precipitate 'scale' that can interfere with sewerage systems.

TASK — IS HARD WATER GOOD FOR YOUR HEALTH?

Although inconvenient in a number of ways, hard water is not a health hazard, and it often tastes rather better than soft water. There have been some claims that hard water might actually benefit health. Calcium and magnesium are essential minerals in our diet, and in areas where the water is very hard, drinking water may provide a substantial amount of the dietary needs.

In recent years, there have been other claims about the health benefits of hard water, such as:

'Hard water has some fantastic health benefits that seem to encourage longer life expectancy and improved health'.

The evidence for these health claims needs to be examined:

- People living in hard water areas across the world seem to have lower rates of heart disease and the proportion of people dying from heart disease is less than that in soft water areas.
- The differences in heart disease in hard and soft water areas are quite small, and some studies have found no link at all.
- There are a number of other diseases which are more common in soft water areas, and at least some of these diseases are not thought to be linked with the drinking water.
- Four controlled experimental studies have shown no link between either water hardness in general or calcium levels in water, and heart disease.
- Seven controlled experiments have looked at the effects of magnesium in drinking water on the amount of heart disease. While results were mixed, overall there does seem to be a protective effect against heart disease if the magnesium level in the water is 10 mg/l or greater.

The World Health Organisation (WHO) has concluded that:

'Although a number of epidemiological studies have shown a statistically significant inverse relationship between the hardness of drinking water and cardiovascular disease, the available data are inadequate to permit the conclusion that the association is causal'.

Questions

1 Rewrite the WHO's conclusions in your own words.
2 Why do you think the fact that hard water areas of the world tend to have lower rates of heart disease than soft water areas is considered rather weak evidence for the hypothesis that drinking hard water reduces heart disease?

Discussion Point

On the basis of the evidence, do you think there is a case for adding calcium and magnesium salts to drinking water in soft water areas?

How do scientists find out what chemicals are present in water?

Figure 13.16 An atomic absorption spectrometer.

We have already seen that gas chromatography is one method that can detect small amounts of chemicals in water. Analytical chemists can also find out which atoms or ions are present in water and their concentrations by using a technique called **atomic spectroscopy**. This technique is not just restricted to water though; it can identify the atoms in all sorts of different samples (for example, in biological tissues). It uses the interaction of electromagnetic radiation (such as X-rays, ultra-violet and visible light) with atoms, and detects this with a machine called a **spectrometer**. These are of various types:

- atomic absorption spectrometers
- optical spectrometers
- X-ray fluorescence spectrometers.

All types can detect and measure very small quantities of atoms or ions.

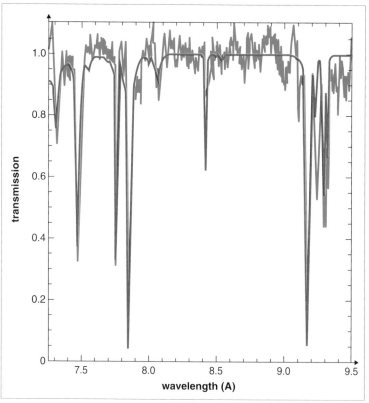

Figure 13.17 The type of read-out an atomic absorption spectrometer produces.

Chapter summary

○ The public water supply is treated using sedimentation, filtration and chlorination.

○ It is important to conserve water in domestic, commercial and industrial contexts.

○ Sea water can be desalinated to supply drinking water.

○ Water and other miscible liquids, for example ethanol, can be separated by distillation.

○ Pigments such as inks can be separated using paper chromatography due to the differing solubilities of the different pigments.

○ The distance a solute travels during the chromatography process is measured using R_f values.

○ Gas chromatography is used by analytical chemists to identify and measure small amounts of certain chemicals, e.g. pollutants in water or in the air and banned substances in the blood of athletes.

○ The solubility of solutes changes with temperature.

○ Hardness in water is caused by calcium and magnesium salts.

○ Hardness can be temporary or permanent.

○ The type and amount of hardness in water can be determined using its ability to create a lather with soap.

○ Boiling, adding sodium carbonate and ion exchange columns can soften water.

○ Hard water has negative effects on boilers and water pipes, but may have some health benefits.

○ Atomic spectroscopy is used by analytical chemists to identify and find the concentrations of atoms or ions, for example metal ions in water samples and biological tissues.

Simple electrical circuits

Solar panels – 'free' energy from the Sun?

Solar panels are really amazing. Light from the Sun (it doesn't even have to be sunny) falls on a specially prepared silicon surface and the energy is absorbed by the silicon atoms in the surface of the panel. This releases 'free' electrons into the panel which generate a current, producing a voltage.

Figure 14.1 Solar panels on the roof of a domestic house.

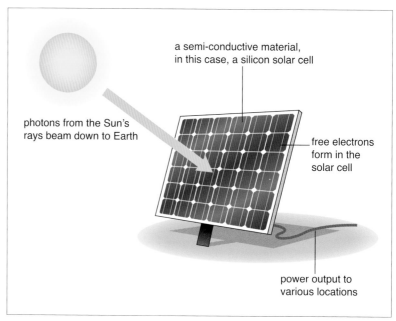

a semi-conductive material, in this case, a silicon solar cell

photons from the Sun's rays beam down to Earth

free electrons form in the solar cell

power output to various locations

Figure 14.2 How electricity is generated in a solar panel.

The electricity that is generated can then be fed directly into the house for use by the occupants, or if excess electricity is generated this can be exported to the National Grid. The National Grid will pay the household for any electricity generated. The solar panel is connected in parallel with the mains supply from the National Grid and a connection box is needed to match the electricity generated by the solar panel with the domestic circuits. An average solar panel system will cost around £12 000, but the savings can be considerable. Approximately 1 tonne of carbon dioxide a year can be saved, and a 2.2 kW system can generate around 40% of a household's yearly electricity needs. The Feed-in Tariff from the National Grid could generate savings and income of around £900 per year, so knowing a little bit about electrical circuits could save you a lot of money and substantially reduce your carbon footprint.

Simple electrical circuits

The circuit diagrams in Figures 14.3 and 14.4 show the simplest of circuits. Figure 14.3 shows a **series** circuit and Figure 14.4 shows a **parallel** circuit. Both circuits have an ammeter connected in series with the battery to record the current. Components are connected in series when they are connected one after another in a continuous loop, so that **all** the current passes through one component, then the next. In parallel circuits, two or more components are connected to the same points in the circuit and the current splits, with some flowing through each component.

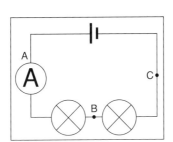

Figure 14.3 A series circuit (circuit A).

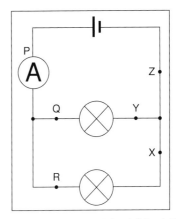

Figure 14.4 A parallel circuit (circuit B).

The **current** in a circuit is a measure of the rate of flow of the negatively charged electrons around the circuit. Current is measured by connecting an ammeter into the circuit, in series with other components, such as bulbs and batteries. The circuit symbol for an ammeter is shown in Figure 14.5.

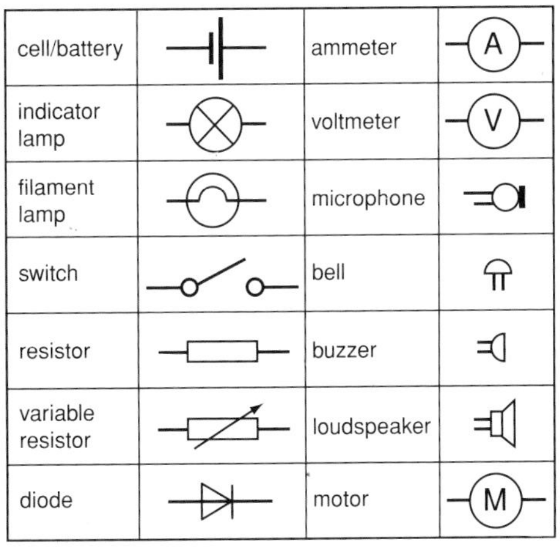

cell/battery	—⊣⊢—	ammeter	—(A)—
indicator lamp	—(⊗)—	voltmeter	—(V)—
filament lamp	—(⌒)—	microphone	⊐◖
switch	—o⁄ o—	bell	⏛
resistor	—▭—	buzzer	⊐◁
variable resistor	—▭⁄—	loudspeaker	⊐◁◖
diode	—▷⊢—	motor	—(M)—

Figure 14.5 Circuit symbols.

Current is measured in amperes, normally shortened to amps, with the symbol A. Mains circuits containing components such as heaters, motors and solar panels will have currents in the order of several amps. Electronic circuits, such as the circuits in computers, will have currents of the order of milliamps, mA (where 1 mA = 0.001 A), or even microamps, μA (where 1 μA = 0.000 001 A).

MEASURING CURRENTS IN SERIES AND PARALLEL CIRCUITS

In this activity you will use an ammeter to measure the current in series and parallel circuits containing the same components. You need to look for patterns in the current readings in different parts of each circuit.

This activity helps you with:
★ working as a team
★ setting up simple electrical circuits
★ measuring currents using ammeters
★ identifying patterns in measurements and observations.

Apparatus
* batteries and holder
* connecting wires
* light bulbs × 2
* ammeter

 Risk assessment

Your teacher will give you a suitable risk assessment for this task.

Procedure
1 Set up Circuit A as in Figure 14.3.
2 Draw a copy of the circuit diagram.
3 Use the ammeter to measure the current at each point, A, B and C, in the diagram. In each case you will need to break the circuit at the point and connect the ammeter in series. Make sure that you connect the ammeter correctly: the + terminal on the ammeter connects in series to the + terminal on the battery – if you are uncertain about this ask your teacher for help.
4 Record the current next to each point on your circuit diagram.
5 Repeat the experiment for the parallel Circuit B (Figure 14.4), measuring and recording the currents at P, Q and R; and X, Y and Z.

Looking for current patterns in the circuits
Series circuits (Circuit A) – study the current values at A, B and C. You should find that they are either all the same, or **very** close to each other.
The current in a series circuit is the same for all components in the circuit.
Parallel circuits (Circuit B) – add the current at Q to the current at R. Compare this value to the current at P – you should find that they are **very** close to each other. Add the current at X to the current at Y, and compare this value to the current at Z.

In parallel circuits, the total (sum) of the currents going into a junction is the same as the total (sum) of the currents out of the junction. This result was first described by Gustav Kirchoff in 1845:

total current into junction = total current out of junction

QUESTIONS

1 Study the following circuits. Use your knowledge of the behaviour of current in series and parallel circuits to calculate the current at each of the marked points on the circuit diagrams (a to j in Figure 14.6).

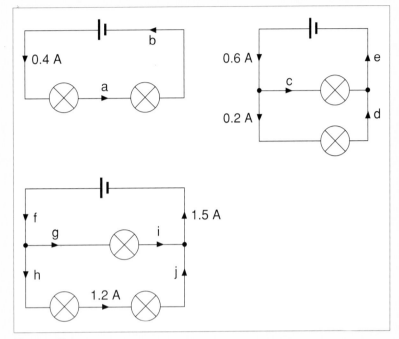

Figure 14.6

2 In a domestic house, all the electrical sockets, and all the domestic appliances such as an electric oven, are connected in parallel to the main circuit board. In one such house during the early evening, the lights are using 2.5 A, a television 0.5 A, an electric oven 13 A and a kettle 10 A. What is the total current drawn from the main circuit board?

3 Draw circuits showing the following:
   a Two bulbs and a switch in series with a 6 V power supply unit.
   b A solar cell connected in parallel with two filament lamps, each one with its own switch in series.

Voltage

Electric current is a measure of the flow of electricity around a circuit. A higher current means that more negatively charged electrons are flowing past a point in the circuit per second. The amount of electrical energy carried per unit charge of electrons is called **voltage**. Voltage is measured in volts, V, by a **voltmeter**. Voltmeters work by measuring the difference in the electrical energy carried by the electrons before the component and after the component. This means that the voltmeters are always connected in parallel with components. Figure 14.7 shows a voltmeter measuring the voltage across a component in a series circuit.

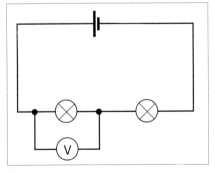

Figure 14.7 A voltmeter measuring voltage across a bulb.

This activity helps you with:
★ working as a team
★ setting up simple electrical circuits
★ measuring currents using ammeters
★ identifying patterns in measurements and observations.

Apparatus
* batteries and holder
* connecting wires
* 3 light bulbs
* voltmeter

In this activity you will use a voltmeter to measure the voltages involved with series and parallel circuits. All components in circuits, such as batteries and bulbs, have a voltage across them which can be easily measured with a voltmeter. But in some cases, for example connecting wires, the voltage is very small, and is often too small to be measured by a standard student laboratory voltmeter. However, the combined effect of several wires may lead to some voltage being 'missed' in a circuit because it is difficult to measure.

Risk assessment

Your teacher will give you a suitable risk assessment for this task.

Procedure

1 Set up the series circuit shown in Figure 14.8.

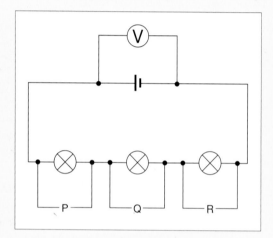

Figure 14.8

2 Measure and record the voltage **in** to the circuit from the battery.
3 Measure and record the voltages **out** of the circuit at points P, Q and R.
4 Add up all the voltages **out** of the circuit. Compare this total voltage out of the circuit to the voltage **in** to the circuit measured across the battery.
5 Taking into account voltages across wires and connections, your voltage in should (approximately) equal the voltage out. This leads to a general circuit law, which states that for a series circuit, the total voltage in to the circuit = total voltage out of the circuit.

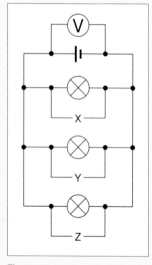

Figure 14.9

6 Now set up the circuit shown in Figure 14.9.
7 Measure and record the voltage **in** to the circuit across the battery.
8 Disconnect the voltmeter and connect it across X, then Y then Z.
9 At each connection X, Y and Z, measure and record the voltage **out** of the circuit.
10 You will find that the voltage **in** to the circuit is the same as the voltage **out** of the circuit across **each** branch of the parallel circuit, that is, the voltage across the battery is the same as the voltage across each bulb.

1 How are the lights in your kitchen (or lounge) at home connected? Can you draw a circuit diagram showing how they (and their switches) are connected to your mains fuse board? Do all the lights have the same operating voltage and power (measured in watts)? Domestic electricity circuits are usually connected in a 'ring main'. Find out what this means and why domestic circuits are connected this way.

2 Being an electrician or an electrical engineer is a really good job. You can work for yourself or for a company. There are a great many opportunities at many different academic levels. Use the following links to find out more about careers involving electricity:
www.careerswales.com
www.connexions-direct.com

QUESTIONS

4 A 12 V solar panel is used to run three household bulbs as shown in Figure 14.10.

  a Bethany connected a voltmeter across the solar cell. What voltage would she measure during the day?

  b Explain why her voltmeter would read 0 V at midnight.

  c During the day, Bethany connected the voltmeter across points A and B in the circuit and turned on switch 1. What would her voltmeter read?

  d Explain why the lighting circuit has three switches. What does each switch do?

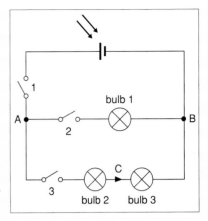

Figure 14.10

  e Give an example (from your house) of a circuit like this where two bulbs work off the same switch.

  f What is the advantage of connecting bulb 1 with one switch compared to bulbs 2 and 3 which have one switch between them?

  g If bulb 2 and bulb 3 are exactly the same (same power rating and brightness), what voltage would Bethany measure if she closed all the switches and connected her voltmeter across points A and C in the circuit?

  h Why would the voltage rating of bulb 1 be different from the voltage ratings of bulbs 2 and 3?

5 Measuring voltages in simple circuits in school is quite safe.

  a Why do electricians have to be much more careful when they are measuring voltages across components in a household wiring circuit?

  b What precautions do you think that they can take to minimise the risks to themselves?

  c Why is it always a good idea to ask an electrician to do electrical work on your house, if you don't really know what you are doing?

Controlling current with resistance

When a voltage is applied across a conductor, an electric current will flow through the conductor. The bigger the voltage applied, the bigger the current. This is very useful when it comes to controlling the electrical power to devices, but mains devices, such as kettles, toasters and vacuum cleaners, are restricted to the 230 V supplied by the mains supply. If we want to control the current being supplied to a device, for example if we want to have two heat settings on a hairdryer, then we have to find another way of varying the current, without changing the voltage. This is where knowing and controlling the **resistance** of the circuit is useful.

Electrical resistance is the property of electrical conductors that opposes the flow of current through it. Materials and components that have a high resistance will only allow a small current to flow through them. Resistance is measured in **ohms**, Ω. Components in electronic circuits work at low current, typically a few milliamps (1 mA = 0.001 A), and so they tend to have high resistance, typically kilohms, kΩ (1 kΩ = 1000 Ω). Insulating components, such as the casing of a laptop, or a mobile phone, are made from materials such as plastics, glass and ceramics, and have very high resistance, often thousands of megohms, MΩ (1 MΩ = 1 000 000 Ω).

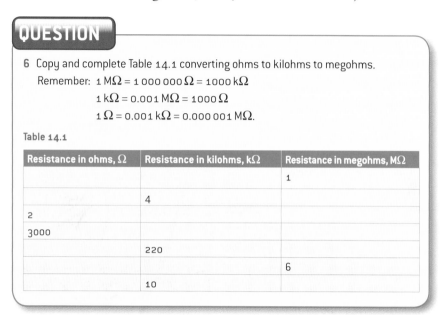

QUESTION

6 Copy and complete Table 14.1 converting ohms to kilohms to megohms.

Remember: 1 MΩ = 1 000 000 Ω = 1000 kΩ

1 kΩ = 0.001 MΩ = 1000 Ω

1 Ω = 0.001 kΩ = 0.000 001 MΩ.

Table 14.1

Resistance in ohms, Ω	Resistance in kilohms, kΩ	Resistance in megohms, MΩ
		1
	4	
2		
3000		
	220	
		6
	10	

Where does resistance come from?

When electrons move through a conductor, like copper wire, they frequently collide with the copper atoms and themselves. The collisions prevent the electrons moving freely through the wire – this is the resistance of the wire. More frequent collisions means higher resistance.

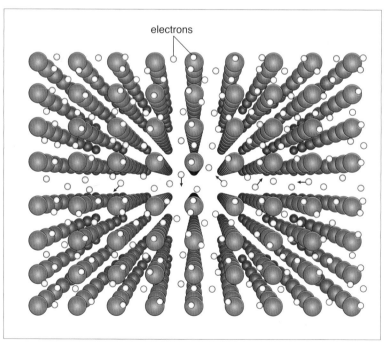

Figure 14.11 Regular lattice of atoms with electrons moving through it.

Insulators, with very high resistance, have very few electrons that are able to move through the structure.

Using resistors to control current and voltage in circuits

Variable resistors are simple components that can be put into circuits to control the current and voltage in the circuit. The circuit picture and circuit diagram in Figure 14.12 show a variable resistor controlling the current through and the voltage across a fixed resistor.

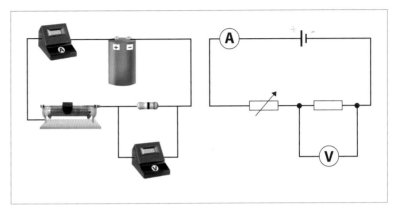

Figure 14.12 A variable resistor controlling current through and voltage across a fixed resistor. Both diagrams show exactly the same circuit – one is a 'picture' and one is a 'circuit diagram'. **When you draw circuits on paper, use the correct circuit symbols on a circuit diagram**.

PRACTICAL · MEASURING CURRENT AND VOLTAGE IN CIRCUITS CONTROLLED BY A VARIABLE RESISTOR

This activity helps you with:
★ working in a pair
★ setting up more complicated electrical circuits
★ measuring and recording current and voltages
★ plotting electrical characteristic graphs (voltage against current).

Apparatus
* DC power supply set on 6 V (or battery pack)
* connecting leads
* large variable resistor (sometimes called a **rheostat**)
* ammeter
* voltmeter
* fixed resistor (about the same resistance as the maximum resistance of the variable resistor)
* low resistance 6 V bulb

Changing the resistance of the variable resistor in the circuit above will alter the current flowing through and the voltage across the fixed resistor. In this practical you will perform this experiment and examine the patterns of current and voltage that you get when you change the resistance of the variable resistor.

Procedure
1 Using the apparatus supplied, connect up the circuit shown in Figure 14.12.
2 Move the slider across the variable resistor until the ammeter measures its largest value. Record this value.
3 Move the slider across to the other end of the variable resistor until the ammeter measures its smallest value. Record this value.
4 Take and record five measurements of current and voltage spread out across the current range for the fixed resistor.
5 Repeat the experiment for a low resistance light bulb, instead of the fixed resistor.

Analysing your results
1 Graphs of voltage against current for components are called 'electrical characteristics'. Plot electrical characteristic graphs for the fixed resistor and the bulb. If you can, plot them both on the same graph using the same axes.
2 Describe in words the pattern of each graph. This means that you have to describe how the voltage (on the y-axis) varies with the current (on the x-axis).
3 Explain how a variable resistor can be used in a circuit to control the current through and the voltage across other components.

Ohm's law

In 1827, a German physicist called Georg Ohm published the results and conclusions about a series of experiments that he had carried out investigating the link between the current and voltage in a simple circuit. He used an early type of battery to apply a voltage to a series of metal wires and he measured the current passing through the wires. Using this apparatus, Ohm discovered that if the temperature of the wires was kept constant, then the size of the current passing through them was directly proportional to the voltage applied across them. Using better apparatus today, this means that if the voltage across a fixed resistor is doubled, then the current through the fixed resistor will also double. Ohm also varied the dimensions and material of the wires that he used and determined that if he kept the voltage constant, then the current was inversely proportional to the resistance of the wire, meaning that if he doubled the resistance of the wire (by doubling its length), then the current halved. Today we summarise Ohm's findings using the equation

$$\text{current, I (amps)} = \frac{\text{voltage, V (volts)}}{\text{resistance, R (ohms)}}$$

$$I = \frac{V}{R}$$

This relationship can be written several different ways:

$$V = I \times R \text{ and}$$

$$R = \frac{V}{I} \text{ or } I = \frac{V}{R}$$

QUESTIONS

7 Using the data that you collected for the Practical: **Measuring current and voltage in circuits controlled by a variable resistor**, construct two tables. One table will be for the fixed resistor data, and the other table will be for the bulb.

Current through component, I (amps)	Voltage across component, V (volts)	Resistance of component, R (ohms / Ω)

8 Describe the patterns in your results for Question 7. How does the resistance of the fixed resistor vary with current (or voltage)? How does the resistance of the bulb vary with current (or voltage)?

QUESTIONS *contd.*

9 A 25 Ω fixed resistor has a current of 2 A through it. Calculate the voltage across the fixed resistor.

10 In a mobile phone circuit, 1.5 V is applied across a keyboard circuit with a resistance of 5000 Ω. What is the current in the keyboard circuit?

11 Figure 14.13 shows the electrical characteristic of a 12 V car bulb. Use the graph to calculate the resistance of the bulb when the current through the bulb is:

a 0.2 A

b 0.6 A

c 1.0 A

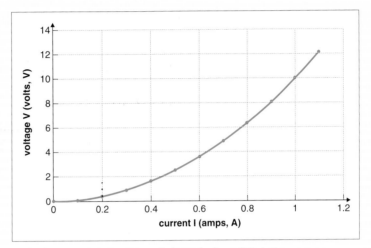

Figure 14.13 An electric characteristic graph of a car light bulb.

12 Explain why the resistance of a bulb changes when more current is passed through it. (*Hint:* when the bulb has more current going through it, it is brighter and **hotter**. How might this affect the structure of the metal filament?)

13 A rheostat (large variable resistor) is set up with a resistance of 12 Ω. A 0–12 V variable power supply is connected in series with an ammeter and the rheostat.

a Draw a circuit diagram of this arrangement.

b Use the data supplied and Ohm's law to determine the current through the rheostat, for voltages of 0 V, 2 V, 4 V, 6 V, 8 V, 10 V and 12 V.

c Plot an electrical characteristic graph of the rheostat. Plot the voltage on the y-axis and the current on the x-axis. Draw a best-fit line through the points and label this line '12 Ω'.

d Calculate the gradient (slope) of the best-fit line. Compare this value to the resistance of the rheostat.

e The resistance of the rheostat is now changed to 6 Ω. On the same electrical characteristic graph, **sketch** the graph for the new resistance setting and label this '6 Ω'. Explain why you have drawn the sketch line where it is.

Electrical power

Power is the general term for the **rate** that a device transforms (changes) energy from one form into other forms; in other words, how much energy it can transform per second. When a device transforms energy, it is said to do **work**. Work is measured in joules, J. Electrical power is therefore the **rate** at which an electrical device, such as a light bulb or a motor, changes electrical energy into other, more useful forms of energy such as light, heat and kinetic energy, so it is the electrical work done per second. Very powerful electrical devices such as power drills, mowers, electric ovens and kettles can convert a large amount of electrical energy per second into other useful forms. Electrical power, like mechanical or thermal (heat) power is measured in watts, W, where $1\,W = 1\,J/s$.

The electrical power of a device can be calculated by multiplying the voltage and the current of the device together:

$$\text{electrical power} = \text{voltage} \times \text{current}$$
$$P = VI$$

Examples

Q Calculate the power of a 12 V light bulb with a current of 0.5 A flowing through it.

A $P = VI = 12 \times 0.5 = 6\,W$

Q A 220 V mower has a power of 2000 W. Calculate the current flowing through the mower.

A $P = VI$ so $I = \dfrac{P}{V} = \dfrac{2000}{220} = 9.1\,A$

Current, resistance and power

If $P = VI$ and $V = IR$

Then, substituting for V in the power equation gives:

$P = (IR) \times I = I^2R$ or

$\text{power} = \text{current}^2 \times \text{resistance}$

This is a really useful equation for calculating the power consumption of electrical components in more complex circuits. Measure the current flowing through a component, square this value and then multiply by its resistance and you have the power of the component.

Example

Q A 400 Ω resistor has a current of 0.75 A flowing through it. Calculate the power of the resistor.

A $P = I^2R = (0.75)^2 \times 400 = 225\,W$

QUESTIONS

14 Calculate the power of a 6 V torch bulb drawing a current of 0.8 A.

15 A current of 5 A passes through a lamp with a resistance of 2.4 Ω, and then through a small cooling fan of resistance 4 Ω. Calculate the power of each component and hence calculate the total power drawn from the circuit.

16 Study the circuit diagram in Figure 14.14.
   a Calculate the power of each bulb.
   b Calculate the total power drawn from the power supply.
   c Calculate the voltage of the power supply.
   d Calculate the voltage across each bulb.

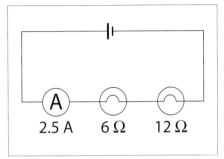

Figure 14.14

17 A mains hairdryer operates with a voltage of 220 V.
   a Calculate the power when it is on its HIGH setting, drawing a current of 8 A.
   b The LOW setting operates with a power of 1 kW (1000 W). Calculate the current flowing through the hairdryer.
   c The hairdryer can also be used in the United States where the mains voltage is different. The power given out by the hairdryer is the same as in the UK (your answer to part a), but the current flowing through the hairdryer is 16 A. Calculate the voltage of the mains in the USA.

Chapter summary

○ Components in an electric circuit can be connected in series or in parallel.
○ In series, the components are connected one after another so that all the current passes through each component.
○ In parallel circuits, two or more components are connected to the same points in the circuit, and the current splits so that some flows through each of the components in parallel.
○ The current in a circuit is a measure of the rate of flow of the negatively charged electrons round the circuit.
○ Current is measured by an ammeter which is connected in series in the circuit.
○ The unit for current is the ampere, or amp for short.
○ The current in a series circuit is the same for all components in the circuit.
○ In parallel circuits, the sum of the currents going into a junction is the same as the currents coming out of the junction.
○ The electrical energy carried by the moving electrons in a circuit is called voltage.
○ Voltage is measured in volts, V, by a voltmeter connected in parallel across the component of the circuit where the voltage is being measured.

○ Electrical resistance is the property of electrical conductors that opposes the flow of current through the conductor. Materials and components that have a high resistance will only allow a small current to flow through them.

○ Resistance is measured in ohms, Ω.

○ Variable resistors are components that can be connected in circuits to control the current and voltage in the circuit.

○ The current flowing through a component depends on the voltage applied across it: the larger the voltage, the larger the current.

○ current = voltage/resistance or $I = V/R$.

○ This can also be written as $V = IR$ and $R = V/I$.

○ Electrical power is the rate at which an electrical device, for example a light bulb or motor, changes electrical energy into other forms of energy, i.e. the electrical work done per second.

○ Electrical power is measured in watts, W, where $1\,W = 1\,J/s$.

○ $P = VI$, and $V = IR$ so $P = I^2R$.

○ $P = I^2R$ can be used to calculate the power consumption of electrical components.

Distance, speed and acceleration

Fastest animals

The fastest animal on the planet is the peregrine falcon (Figure 15.1). When the peregrine falcon is on its hunting dive, called a 'stoop', it soars to great heights and then dives almost vertically at speeds of over 200 mph or nearly 90 m/s! However, it does not even make the top ten fastest birds when travelling in level flight. The spine-tailed swift (Figure 15.2) is the fastest bird in level flight and can fly at 106 mph or 47 m/s.

Figure 15.1 Peregrine falcon.

Figure 15.2 Spine-tailed swift.

Measuring speeds

Speed is a measure of how fast or slow an object or animal is moving. A speed of 0 m/s means that the object is stationary, or not moving. In order to calculate speed, we need to know about two other quantities: the **distance** that the object moves (measured in metres, m) and the **time** that the object took to travel the distance (measured in seconds, s).

The speed of the object can then be calculated by the equation:

$$\text{speed} = \frac{\text{distance}}{\text{time}}$$

Figure 15.3 shows how an equation triangle can be used to calculate one of the quantities in the equation if the other two are known.

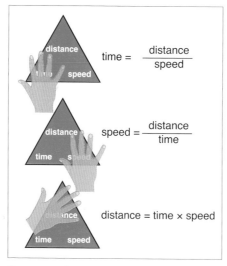
$$\text{time} = \frac{\text{distance}}{\text{speed}}$$

$$\text{speed} = \frac{\text{distance}}{\text{time}}$$

$$\text{distance} = \text{time} \times \text{speed}$$

Examples

Q A diving peregrine falcon will cover 200 m in 2.2 seconds. Calculate the speed of the falcon.

A $\text{speed} = \dfrac{\text{distance}}{\text{time}} = \dfrac{200}{2.2} = 91 \, \text{m/s}$

Q How far can a spine-tailed swift travel in 1 minute (60 s) if it flies at 47 m/s?

A $\text{speed} = \dfrac{\text{distance}}{\text{time}}$ so distance $= \text{speed} \times \text{time} = 47 \times 60 = 2820 \, \text{m} = 2.82 \, \text{km}$

TASK   THE ANIMAL OLYMPICS 100 M FINAL

The 100 m final in the Animal Olympics would be a curious contest. The rules say that only one animal from each animal group can enter. This is how they would line up.

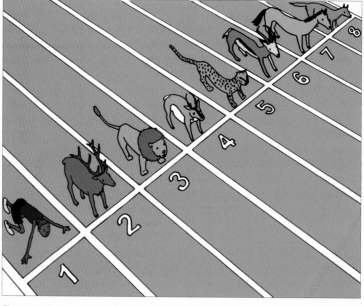

Figure 15.4 The 100 m Animal Olympics final.

When running at top speed, these animals have the speeds as shown in Table 15.1.

Table 15.1 Top speeds.

Animal	Top speed		
	mph	km/h	m/s
Cheetah	70	113	31
Pronghorn antelope	61	98	27
Lion	50	80	22
Springbok	50	80	22
Horse	48	77	21
Elk	45	72	20
Coyote	43	69	19
Usain Bolt	43	69	19

1 Each animal finishes the 100 m race. Use the data to calculate the times for each competitor.

2 Explain why, in reality, the times for each competitor will be higher than those that you have calculated.

3 Usain Bolt broke the World 100 m record in the Beijing Olympic final in 2008, and this record breaking run has been one of the most closely analysed runs in history, although he subsequently broke his own world record in the 2009 World Championships. Usain Bolt's mean times for the 2008 final race were as shown in Table 15.2.

a Make a copy of this table, but add a third column labelled 'Mean speed, m/s'. Calculate Usain Bolt's mean speed for each 10 m segment of the race and fill in your table.

b Plot a graph of Usain Bolt's mean speed (on the y-axis) against distance (on the x-axis). Take the mean speed to occur in the middle of each 10 m segment of the race, so plot the distances as: 5 m, 15 m, 25 m and so on up to 95 m.

c Describe the pattern (or shape) of the graph and try to explain how mean speed varies with distance.

d In 2009, the Cincinnati Zoo's 8-year-old female cheetah Sarah became the world's fastest land mammal. Sarah covered 100 m in a time of 6.13 seconds, breaking the previous mark of 6.19 seconds set by a male South African cheetah named Nyana in 2001. Use this information (assuming that a cheetah will have a similar pattern of running to Usain Bolt) to sketch on the same graph the pattern for Sarah compared with Usain Bolt.

Table 15.2 Usain Bolt's split times in the 2008 Olympic finals.

Distance (m)	Split time (s)
reaction time to leave blocks	0.165
0–10 (including reaction time)	1.85
10–20	1.02
20–30	0.91
30–40	0.87
40–50	0.85
50–60	0.82
60–70	0.82
70–80	0.82
80–90	0.83
90–100	0.90
0–100	9.69

Discussion Points

1 You can find lots of videos of Usain Bolt's 2008 Olympic 100 m final online. Watch the race. It almost feels as if he is slowing down at the end and waving to the crowd, yet in reality he's still running at top speed. How much faster do you think human beings can run? Is there going to be an ultimate 'top speed' or do you think that humans will get progressively quicker and quicker?

2 The cheetah has a substantially faster top speed than most of its prey (for example the springbok), yet it only has a 50% kill success rate. Why do you think that half of the cheetah's prey get away?

Speed or velocity?

If speed is just a measure of how fast or how slow something is moving, how do we distinguish between speeds in different directions? The Animal Olympics 100 m final would be chaos if all the competitors ran off in different directions! The 100 m event (and all running competitions) work because everyone is running the same way. To distinguish between motion in different directions we have to use a different quantity called **velocity**, given the symbol v, and measured in m/s with a given direction. Velocity is a **vector** quantity which means that it has magnitude (or size) but also direction (up, down, left, right, north or south, etc). Speed is a **scalar** quantity, because it only has magnitude (size) and no direction. Using velocity, we can easily distinguish between the motion of 10 m/s, north, and 10 m/s, south. Both motions have the same speed, but they have opposite velocities.

There are many cases where velocity is much more important than speed. Suppose you are on a Duke of Edinburgh (D of E) walk in the Brecon Beacons. If your assessor asks you to walk with a mean velocity of 0.5 m/s west towards a checkpoint 2 km away, she will expect you to be at the checkpoint in about 4000 seconds or just over an hour. If you walk at 0.5 m/s in **any** direction, she would have to search everywhere in a 2 km radius from where you started, i.e. a round trip of about 25 km. You could be seriously lost in the time it would take her to search for you!

Acceleration: speeding up and slowing down

When objects speed up they accelerate. When they slow down they decelerate. But is acceleration about change in speed, or should we really be talking about changes in velocity? Acceleration is also a vector quantity (because we can accelerate or decelerate, and sometimes the acceleration can be at right angles to the motion, as with objects moving in a circle or in orbit). This means we must define acceleration in terms of velocity, rather than speed, so part of determining acceleration involves measuring a change in velocity. When determining acceleration we also need to think about the time taken for the velocity to change. For example, a coyote and Usain Bolt have the same top speed (about 12 m/s), but a coyote is much less massive than Usain Bolt. An adult male coyote can have a mass up to about 22 kg, whereas Usain Bolt has a mass of about 94 kg – over 4 times higher. Although they can have the same change in velocity (0 m/s to 12 m/s = 12 m/s), the coyote will take much less time to get to its maximum velocity so it will have a much greater acceleration. (The effect of mass on the acceleration of objects is covered in more detail in Chapter 16.)

Acceleration can be defined using the equation:

$$\text{acceleration (or deceleration)} = \frac{\text{change in velocity}}{\text{time}} = \frac{\Delta v}{t}$$

The units of acceleration are metres per second per second, or metres per second squared, m/s^2.

Example

Q In Table 15.2, Usain Bolt got to his fastest speed (12 m/s) in the 2008 100 m Olympic final after about 5.5 s from the start gun. What was his acceleration?

A acceleration $= \dfrac{\text{change in velocity}}{\text{time}} = \dfrac{\Delta v}{t} = \dfrac{(12 - 0)}{5.5} = 2.2 \, \text{m/s}^2$

QUESTION

1 The performance of very fast cars is important. Manufacturers spend a great deal of time and money testing the performance, so that the numbers can be used to advertise and sell the cars. The standard way of testing acceleration is to measure the time that the car takes to get from rest to 100 km/h (27.8 m/s). The higher the performance of the car, the shorter the time that it takes. Table 15.3 shows some data for some of the world's fastest production cars, and for comparison, a standard Ford Focus 1.8. Copy and complete the table (without the pictures) by calculating the acceleration of each car.

Table 15.3 Data for some of the world's fastest cars.

Car	Time (s) to reach 100 km/h (27.7 m/s) from a standing start	Acceleration (m/s²)
Bugatti Veyron Super Sport	2.4	
Ariel Atom V8	2.5	
Porsche 911 Turbo S	2.7	
Nissan GT-R	2.8	
Maclaren MP4-12C	3.1	
Ford Focus 1.8	10.3	

2 Travelling on a motorway, HGV lorries are usually speed limited to 60 mph or 27 m/s. A Ford Focus 1.8 travelling behind an HGV lorry travelling at 27 m/s accelerates to 70 mph or 31 m/s in 2 seconds, in order to overtake the HGV lorry. What is the acceleration of the Ford Focus? How does this compare with its maximum acceleration?

Graphs of motion

When analysing the motion of objects it is very useful to plot graphs showing how one quantity varies with another. The simplest graph of motion is a distance–time graph.

Figure 15.11 shows the distance–time graph for Usain Bolt's 2008 World record 100 m Olympic final.

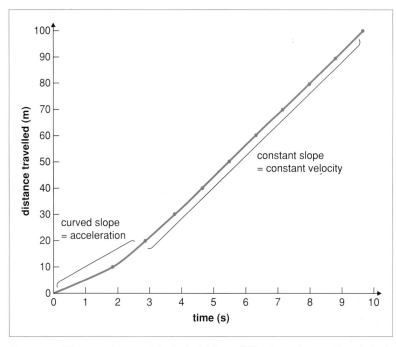

Figure 15.5 Distance–time graph for Usain Bolt's 2008 World record 100 m Olympic final.

We can see from the graph that for most of the race, Usain was travelling at (approximately) constant velocity – we can tell this because, from about 2.5 s into the race until the end, the graph is a straight line with constant slope so the distance travelled per second was about the same. For the first 2.5 seconds Usain was accelerating out away from his blocks and the graph curves upwards, indicating that his velocity is increasing.

On a distance–time graph:

- Stationary objects are shown by flat straight lines.
- Objects travelling at constant velocity are shown by straight sloping lines.
- The speed of an object can be found by measuring the slope or gradient of the graph.
- Objects that are accelerating (or decelerating) are shown by curved lines.

Example

Q Between 2.5 s and 9.69 s, Usain Bolt was travelling at constant mean velocity. The distance that he travelled in this time was 85 m. Calculate his mean velocity.

A mean velocity $= \dfrac{\text{total distance travelled}}{\text{time taken}} = \dfrac{85}{(9.69 - 2.5)} = 11.8 \, \text{m/s}$

QUESTIONS

3 Describe the motion of the objects illustrated by the distance–time graphs (a), (b) and (c) in Figure 15.6.

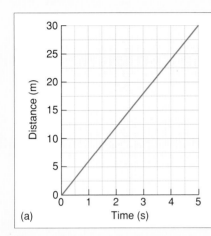
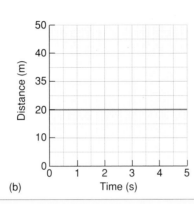
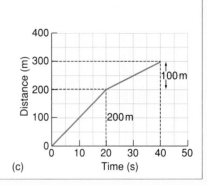

Figure 15.6

4 Calculate the mean velocity of the object moving in (a).

5 Calculate the TWO mean velocities illustrated by distance–time graph (c).

6 Sketch distance–time graphs for the following:

   a An object moving 20 m in 4 s, then stationary for 3 s, then moving back to the start in 8 s.

   b An object stationary for 2 s then moving at a constant velocity of 5 m/s for 10 s, then stationary for another 2 s.

   c An object moving 10 m in 5 s, then moving in the same direction at a constant velocity of 4 m/s for 3 s, then moving back to the start in 4 s.

PRACTICAL — MEASURING, PLOTTING AND ANALYSING REAL DISTANCE–TIME GRAPHS

This activity helps you with:

★ working as a large team
★ collecting movement data
★ measuring distances and times
★ plotting distance–time graphs of motion
★ analysing distance–time graphs.

Real distance–time graphs can be plotted by taking careful measurements of the motion of moving objects. In this activity you will collect data from the motion of students running, cycling or walking over a set distance. You will need to work as a large team and you will need to have access to a playground or a sports field.

⚠ Risk assessment

Your teacher will provide you with a suitable risk assessment. If you are asthmatic or have other medical conditions that could be affected by exercise, tell your teacher.

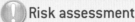

continued...

Apparatus
* open space, for example a playground or sports field
* lots of stop watches
* a long tape measure or a trundle wheel
* clipboards, paper and pens/pencils to record information
* students who are willing to run/walk/cycle
* PE cones

Procedure
1 Find a suitable open space to perform the experiment.
2 Measure the length of the space and divide the length into roughly six equally spaced intervals (say 5 m). Record the distance between the intervals.
3 Place a PE cone at each interval (e.g. one at the start, one at 5 m, one at 10 m and so on).
4 Stand three students with stop watches next to each cone, and have one student at the start to act as 'Starter'.
5 The volunteer students who will run/walk/cycle then take it in turns to move up the course. When the starter starts each volunteer, all the students who are timing start their stop watches, and then stop them when the volunteer passes their cone. Each timing student records how far they are from the start, and the time of each volunteer to get to them.
6 This task can be repeated several times with several different ways of moving. Each person timing needs to make sure that they record and label each way of moving correctly in the right order. You may want to use a numbering system.
7 Once back in the laboratory, all timing students pool their results. This is best done by one student or the teacher using a spreadsheet such as Excel.

Analysing your results
1 For each method of moving, calculate the mean time of the volunteer to get to each cone.
2 Use your data to compile a table of distance and mean time for each.
3 Plot distance (y-axis) against mean time (x-axis) graphs for each volunteer's way of moving.
4 Label any portions of each graph that correspond to 'acceleration', 'deceleration', 'constant velocity' or 'stationary'.
5 Calculate any suitable mean velocities on your graphs and write these values on your graphs.

Velocity–time graphs

Velocity–time graphs are even more useful than distance–time graphs. Not only can you analyse the motion in terms of velocity, but you can also measure accelerations and calculate distances travelled. Figure 15.7 shows the velocity–time graph for Usain Bolt's 2008 Beijing Olympic World record 100 m race.

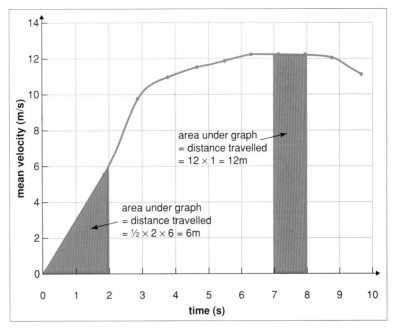

Figure 15.7 Velocity–time graph for Usain Bolt's World record 100 m Olympic title.

You can see that for the first two seconds Usain Bolt was accelerating at a constant rate. The graph is a straight line with a constant slope. We can calculate his acceleration in this period of the race by measuring the gradient of the line.

$$\text{acceleration} = \frac{\text{change in velocity}}{\text{time}} = \frac{(6-0)}{2} = 3\,\text{m/s}^2$$

This is the gradient of the line between 0 s and 2 s. Between 2 s and 3 s, Usain Bolt increased his acceleration. In this time he changed his velocity from 6 m/s to 10 m/s. His acceleration for this portion of the race was:

$$\text{acceleration} = \frac{\text{change in velocity}}{\text{time}} = \frac{(10-6)}{1} = 4\,\text{m/s}^2$$

This is shown on the graph by a steeper line. After about 3 s into the race, Usain's acceleration reduced. For the next 4 s his velocity increased from 10 m/s up to just over 12 m/s, and his acceleration was:

$$\text{acceleration} = \frac{\text{change in velocity}}{\text{time}} = \frac{(12-10)}{4} = 0.5\,\text{m/s}^2$$

Usain then travelled at approximately constant velocity of 12 m/s for the next 1.5 s before decelerating slightly before the finish.

$$\text{deceleration} = \frac{\text{change in velocity}}{\text{time}} = \frac{(11-12)}{1.5} = -0.67\,\text{m/s}^2$$

Note that the deceleration is negative because he is slowing down.
    For **velocity–time** graphs:

- Stationary objects have zero velocity.
- A flat, straight line indicates an object travelling at constant velocity.
- A straight line sloping upwards indicates an object accelerating.

- A straight line sloping downwards indicates an object decelerating.
- The gradient or slope of a velocity–time graph is the acceleration.
- The **area** under the velocity-time graph is the distance travelled.

The distance that Usain Bolt travelled in the first 2 s of the race can be calculated by measuring the area under the velocity–time graph up to this time. The shape is a triangle with a base of 2 s and a height of 6 m/s. The area of a triangle = ½ × base × height.

distance travelled (0 to 2 s) = area under velocity–time graph = ½ × 2 × 6 = 6 m

Between 7 s and 8 s, Usain Bolt was travelling at a constant speed of 12 m/s. The area under the graph is the distance that he travelled in this time interval. The shape under the graph is a rectangle.

distance travelled (7 to 8 s) = area under velocity–time graph = 12 × 1 = 12 m

The total distance that Usain Bolt ran is the total area under the graph, which of course is 100 m.

QUESTION

7 Describe the motion illustrated by the velocity–time graphs in Figure 15.8. For each graph calculate any accelerations/decelerations and (HT only) the total distance travelled.

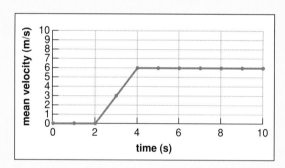

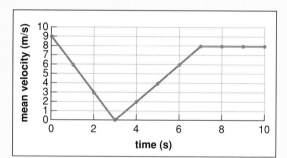

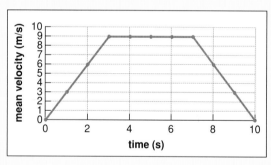

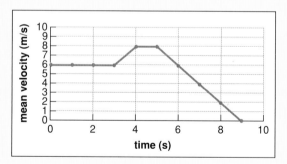

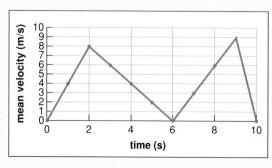

Figure 15.8 Velocity–time graphs.

Chapter summary

○ Speed is a measure of how fast an object or animal is moving.

○ $\text{speed} = \dfrac{\text{distance travelled in metres}}{\text{time taken in seconds}}$

○ Speed is a scalar quantity, that is, it only has magnitude.

○ Velocity is a vector and has direction as well as magnitude.

○ Velocity is measured in metres per second, in a specified direction.

○ Acceleration is the rate of change of velocity. Objects that are going faster are accelerating, and objects that are going slower are decelerating.

○ $\text{acceleration} = \dfrac{\text{change in velocity}}{\text{time}}$ or $a = \dfrac{\Delta r}{t}$

○ The units of acceleration are metres per second squared, m/s^2.

○ On **distance–time** graphs stationary objects are shown by flat straight lines and objects travelling at constant velocity are shown by straight sloping lines.

○ The speed of an object can be found by measuring the slope or gradient of the graph.

○ For **velocity–time** graphs, a flat straight line indicates an object travelling at constant velocity and a straight line sloping upwards indicates an object accelerating. A straight line sloping downwards indicates an object decelerating.

○ The acceleration can be found by measuring the gradient or slope of the velocity–time graph.

○ The area under the velocity–time graph is the distance travelled.

Moving in space

Figure 16.1 The International Space Station.

The International Space Station (ISS) is the largest manned object ever sent into space. The ISS marked its 10th anniversary of human occupation on 2 November 2010. Since the very first mission, on 31 October 2000, the ISS has been visited by 196 astronauts and cosmonauts from eight different countries. Since the anniversary date there have been 103 launches to the space station: 67 Russian vehicles, 34 US Space Shuttles, one European and one Japanese vehicle. A total of 150 spacewalks have been conducted in support of the ISS assembly totalling more than 944 hours. The ISS, including its large solar arrays, spans the area of a rugby pitch, and weighs 375 481 kg. The ISS now has more liveable room than a conventional five-bedroom house, and has two bathrooms and a gym! How did they get all that stuff up into space?

Getting big objects into space

The parts of the ISS have been put up into space by Russian Soyuz space rockets and the Space Shuttle.

Figure 16.2 The Space Shuttle (left) and the Russian Soyuz space rockets.

Discussion Point

What would it be like to live for 180 days on the ISS (a typical mission duration)? What sort of things in your daily routine would be difficult on the ISS in low Earth orbit?

In order to get the rockets up into the air, the huge rocket engines have to generate a thrust force larger than the weight of the rocket, all its fuel and its payload (in this case the payload is parts for the ISS). Weight is a force – the force of gravity acting on the mass of an object. On the surface of the Earth, 1 kg of mass has a weight of 10 N. This is called the **gravitational field strength**, g.

PRACTICAL ANALYSING THE GRAVITATIONAL FIELD STRENGTH OF THE EARTH

This activity helps you with:
★ working with a partner
★ measuring and recording the weight and mass of objects
★ calculating values of g
★ plotting a graph and looking for patterns
★ thinking about the accuracy of measurements.

There is a direct relationship between the mass and the weight of an object – more mass, more weight. In this experiment you will systematically measure the mass and weight of objects and then analyse the link between the two, and use your measurements to calculate the gravitational field strength.

Procedure
1 Make a copy of Table 16.1.
2 Tare the electronic balance (set to zero).
3 Zero each Newton meter.
4 Place the base and hanger of the mass stack on the electronic balance.
5 Measure and record the **mass** in grams. Convert the mass to kg and record in the correct column of the table.
6 Find the lowest range Newton meter that will measure the weight of the base and hanger.
7 Measure and record the **weight** of the base and hanger.
8 Repeat for each added slotted mass.

Apparatus
* Electronic balance
* Selection of Newton meters (e.g. 0–2 N, 0–5 N, 0–10 N, 0–20 N)
* Slotted mass stack

Table 16.1

Number of slotted masses	Mass (g)	Mass (kg) (NB 100 g = 0.1 kg)	Weight (N)	$g = \dfrac{\text{weight (N)}}{\text{mass (kg)}}$
1 (Base and hanger)				
2				
3				
(continue to…)				
10				

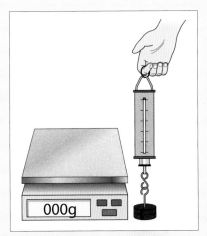

Figure 16.3 Balance and mass stack with Newton meter.

Analysing your results
1 For each slotted mass combination, calculate the sum $\left(g = \dfrac{\text{weight in N}}{\text{mass in kg}}\right)$, and record this in the last column of the table.
2 Look at the values of g that you have calculated – is there a pattern?
3 Calculate the mean value of g.
4 Use the range of the values to state an uncertainty on your value of g, i.e. $g = (\text{mean value} \pm \text{uncertainty})$ N/kg.
5 Plot a graph of weight (N) on the y-axis against mass (kg) on the x-axis.
6 Draw a best-fit straight line through your points (make sure your line goes through the origin).
7 Calculate the gradient (slope) of your best-fit line. Compare your value with the mean value of g that you calculated earlier. The gradient of this line is the value of g.
8 The value of g is approximately 10 N/kg. How close to this value is:
   a your mean calculated value?
   b the gradient of your graph?
✓ 9 How could you use your graph to determine a value of the uncertainty of the value of g?
✓ 10 Why is it more accurate to measure the weight of a slotted mass with a Newton meter with the lowest range capable of measuring it?
✓ 11 Would it be better to measure all the weights with the same (bigger ranged) Newton meter?

When we are living in the Earth's gravitational field we live in a world of 1g, that is, 1 × the Earth's gravitational field. At take-off, the astronauts experience 3g (3 × the Earth's gravitational field strength). In orbit, the astronauts effectively experience 0g. What do you think these gravitational fields 'feel' like?

In the previous practical you found that the weight of an object can be calculated by multiplying the mass of the object (in kg) by the gravitational field strength, g (in N/kg).

weight of object (N) = mass (kg) × gravitational field strength (N/kg)

We can use this relationship to calculate the weight of space vehicles (or any other object). This is useful because if we know the weight of a space vehicle, like a rocket or the Space Shuttle, then we can work out how much thrust force is needed by the engines to balance and then overcome the force of gravity on the mass (that is, the weight) and boost the rocket up into space.

Example

Q The mass of an unloaded Space Shuttle is 78 000 kg. What is its weight?

A weight (N) = mass (kg) × 10 N/kg = 78 000 × 10 = 780 000 N

QUESTIONS

1 A typical ISS module has a mass of 22 700 kg. Each of the two Space Shuttle solid rocket boosters has a lift-off mass of 590 000 kg, and the external fuel tank (filled with rocket fuel) has a lift-off mass of 760 000 kg.
  a Calculate the weight of each component of the Space Shuttle launch system.
  b What is the total lift-off weight of the Space Shuttle launch system?
  c What is the minimum total thrust needed by the Space Shuttle main engines and the solid fuel rocket boosters? Why is this a 'minimum'?

2 The last Space Shuttle launch took place in June 2011. From that point on, the ISS will be serviced via Russian Progress and American Dragon spacecraft whilst astronauts will travel to and from the ISS in Russian Soyuz spacecraft. All Russian spacecraft are launched via Soyuz-2 rockets and the American spacecraft will be launched with Falcon 9 rockets (Table 16.2). Copy and complete the table, calculating the launch weight of each rocket and the minimum resultant upwards force at launch.

Table 16.2

Rocket	Launch mass (kg)	Launch weight (N)	Launch thrust (N)	Minimum resultant upwards force at launch (N)
Falcon 9	340 000		4 500 000	
Soyuz-2	310 000		4 000 000	

Inertia and Newton's first law of motion

The enormous mass of space rocket launch systems means that the thrust force required by the rocket engines has to be huge. The mass of an object dictates how easy (or difficult) it is for an object to move, or how easy or difficult it is to change the motion of an object – this is called **inertia**. Inertia is defined as the resistance of any object to a change in its state of motion or rest. Massive objects such as space rockets have large amounts of inertia. The inertia of an object also explains why it is very difficult to alter the motion of very big objects like the ISS. The ISS has a mass of 400 000 kg, and is in low Earth orbit on average about 350 km above the surface of the Earth, travelling at 7700 m/s (about 17 000 mph). In 1687 Isaac Newton realised that there is a link between the motion of an object and its mass. He summarised this in his first law of motion:

> 'An object at rest stays at rest, or an object in motion stays in motion with the same speed and in the same direction, unless acted upon by an unbalanced force.'

On Earth it is very difficult to observe Newton's first law, because friction always acts to oppose the motion of an object. In space, where friction is zero, it is easy to see the effect of Newton's first law.

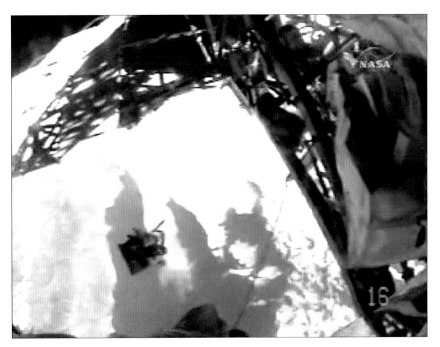

Figure 16.4 Heidemarie Stefanyshyn-Piper's toolbag floating away from the ISS.

This was well illustrated in 2008, when the helmet camera of astronaut Heidemarie Stefanyshyn-Piper caught sight of her toolbag, containing a grease gun that she was supposed to use to lubricate a solar panel on the ISS, floating off into space. The toolbag (about the size of a small briefcase) had somehow become unattached, and due to its inertia it carried on moving away from the astronaut. The toolbag, until it burned up on re-entering the Earth's atmosphere in late 2009, became one of thousands of small bits of space junk in orbit around the Earth, moving in a circular orbit due to the attraction of the force of gravity and moving at the same speed forever, as predicted by Newton's first law of motion.

This activity helps you with:
★ investigating Newton's first law of motion
★ using a datalogger and light gates.

In this investigation your teacher will set up a linear air track and light gate system. The linear air track is an excellent device for showing the motion of objects on Earth, as the moving objects sit on a cushion of air that reduces friction to the point where it is almost negligible.

The linear air track (LAT) will be set up with four light gates equally spread out along the length of the LAT. The light gates and the computer software will measure the velocity of the glider as it passes through them. If Newton's first law is in operation then the velocity of the glider will not change as it moves down the track after a small push.

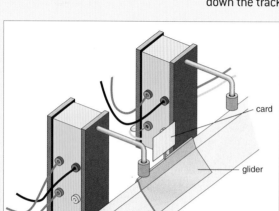

Figure 16.5 Linear air track and glider.

Apparatus
* linear air track and blower
* light gates × 4, datalogger, computer and datalogging software
* glider with short interrupt card

Procedure

1 Measure the width of the interrupt card. You will be asked to enter this value into the datalogger software.
2 Measure the distance of each light gate from the 'start' end of the LAT.
3 Fire the glider down the LAT using the rubber band mounted on the v-prong at the start end of the LAT. Use the software to measure the velocity of the glider through each light gate. If you always push the glider back into the rubber band by the same amount, the glider will always be fired at the same initial velocity.
4 Record the velocity of the glider at each light gate together with its distance from the start of the LAT.
5 If you can, repeat your measurements twice more and calculate the mean velocity of the glider through each light gate.

Analysing your results

1 Plot a graph of **velocity** of the glider (*y*-axis) against **distance** from the start of the LAT (*x*-axis).
2 Draw a best-fit line through your points. If your glider obeys Newton's first law then the velocity of the glider will not change as it travels down the LAT and all the velocities will be exactly the same.
3 Does your glider obey Newton's first law?
4 Why might the velocity of the glider change as it moves down the track?
5 Use your data to decide how repeatable this experiment is.

Further experiments:

1 You can introduce more friction into the experiment by turning down the air blower – what happens then?
2 What happens when you increase the inertia of the glider by stacking masses on it?

You can access a virtual linear air track at www.lon-capa.org/~mmp/kap6/cd157a.htm.

Momentum

Another way to think of inertia is to think about the link between the mass and velocity of a moving object. When Heidemarie Stefanyshyn-Piper's toolbag drifted off whilst she was on a spacewalk servicing the ISS, it went into space near to the ISS. Remember, the ISS is in orbit moving at 7700 m/s, and this means that the toolbag is moving at that speed as well. Imagine the damage that a 5 kg toolbag travelling at 7700 m/s would cause if you hit it travelling in the opposite direction!

Momentum is the name given to the product of the mass and velocity of an object. Objects have large momentum if they are either very massive and/or moving at high velocity.

momentum p (kg m/s) = **mass** m (kg) × **velocity** v (m/s)

$$p = mv$$

QUESTIONS

3 Calculate the momentum of a 5 kg toolbag travelling at 7700 m/s.

4 Calculate the momentum of the ISS (mass = 400 000 kg), also travelling at 7700 m/s.

5 At take-off, the Space Shuttle leaves the launch tower travelling at 45 m/s. The momentum of the Shuttle at this point is 90 000 000 kg m/s. What is the mass of the Shuttle at this point? Why isn't the mass of the Shuttle constant?

6 When the solid rocket boosters and the external fuel tank are jettisoned, the Space Shuttle has a momentum of 140 000 000 kg m/s, and a mass of 100 700 kg. What is the velocity of the Shuttle at this point?

7 Use the mass and momentum information in these questions and the rest of the text to describe how the mass, velocity and momentum of the Shuttle change during its flight up to docking with the ISS. What is the final momentum of the Shuttle just before docking with the ISS?

The forces and motion at take-off

Just before the moment of take-off, the total weight of a space rocket is balanced by the thrust force of the rocket engines. The resultant force is zero. At take-off, as the mass (and therefore the weight) of the rocket starts to decrease (because it is using up fuel), so the resultant force starts to become bigger and bigger in the upwards direction, causing the rocket to lift off and accelerate. Figure 16.6 shows the velocity–time profile for a typical Space Shuttle launch up to T + 500 s (500 s after take-off – the letter T is used to show take-off time).

Discussion Point

A Space Shuttle (mass = 78 000 kg) docks with the ISS (mass = 385 471 kg). At the moment of docking the ISS is effectively stationary and the Space Shuttle is moving at 2 m/s relative to the ISS. What are the relative momentums of the Space Shuttle and the ISS **before** docking, and what is their combined momentum **after** docking? What is the effective increase in speed of the ISS? What does this tell you about momentum and collisions?

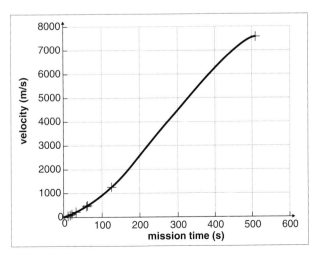

Figure 16.6 How the velocity of the Space Shuttle varies with flight time after take-off.

You saw in Chapter 15 that the gradient (slope) of a velocity–time graph is the acceleration of the object. You will notice from Figure 16.6 that the initial gradient of the graph is quite small in value and it never actually gets much greater than about 2 or 3*g* ($g \approx 10\,\text{m/s}^2$, $2g \approx 20\,\text{m/s}^2$, $3g \approx 30\,\text{m/s}^2$).

What does this graph actually show? Well, something quite fundamental – as the resultant force on the object (the shuttle) starts to increase from zero, so the shuttle starts to accelerate and the bigger the resultant force, the bigger the acceleration.

Isaac Newton first realised the link between acceleration and force in 1687. He summarised the link in his second law of motion, which we now write as:

resultant **force** F (N) = **mass** m (kg) $\times$ **acceleration** a (m/s^2)

$$F = ma$$

PRACTICAL   INVESTIGATING NEWTON'S SECOND LAW

This activity helps you with:

★ investigating Newton's second law
★ making observations of a moving object
★ plotting a graph and analysing the shape
★ calculating quantities from a graph.

Your teacher will set up an experiment to investigate Newton's second law using a linear air track (LAT). The demonstration will show the link between the force applied, mass and acceleration of a LAT glider.

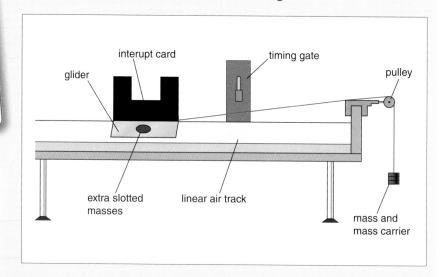

Figure 16.7 Experimental set-up.

Apparatus

* linear air track and blower
* LAT glider with interrupt card (you need to measure and record its dimensions)
* light gate, datalogger and computer running datalogger software that will measure acceleration directly using the shaped interrupt card
* LAT mounted pulley
* 100 g slotted mass stack
* cotton thread
* electronic balance

 Risk assessment

Your teacher will provide you with a suitable risk assessment for this demonstration.

Procedure

1 Attach a suitable length of cotton thread to the glider and tie a loop in the other end to attach to the mass stack holder.
2 Place the rest of the slotted masses onto the holder spikes on the glider.
3 Measure and record the combined mass of the glider (+ slotted masses) and the mass stack holder.
4 Each 100 g slotted mass added to the mass stack holder adds another 1 N resultant force on the glider.

PRACTICAL *contd.*

5 Construct a table to record values of resultant force *F* in N and acceleration *a* in m/s², with a third column in your table to calculate values of force/acceleration.
6 Drape the thread over the pulley (as shown in the diagram), let the mass holder fall and measure and record the acceleration of the glider.
7 Re-set the apparatus and move one slotted mass from the glider to the mass stack (this ensures that the total mass being accelerated remains constant during the experiment).
8 Let go of the mass stack and measure and record the acceleration.
9 Repeat for other values of accelerating force.

Analysing your results
1 Calculate values of force/acceleration in your table and record them.
2 Is there a pattern in your results? What is the mean value of force/acceleration? How does this compare to the mass (in kg) of the glider plus slotted masses?
3 Plot a graph of resultant force (*y*-axis) against acceleration (*x*-axis). Confirm that it is a straight line and draw a best-fit straight line through your results (starting at the origin).
4 Measure and calculate the gradient (slope) of the graph.
5 Compare your gradient to the mass (in kg) of the glider plus the slotted masses.

Your graph should show that force is directly proportional to the acceleration of the glider (and masses), and that the gradient of the line is the mass (in kg) of the moving object. This shows force = mass × acceleration.

QUESTION

8 A fully laden Soyuz spacecraft (mass = 7150 kg) accelerates away from the ISS towards its re-entry point with an acceleration of 2 m/s² relative to the ISS. Calculate the resultant force on the Soyuz spacecraft.

Figure 16.8 Soyuz spacecraft.

9   At lift-off, the combined thrust of the SRB and main Shuttle engines is 30 400 000 N. The total weight of the Space Shuttle at lift-off is 20 407 000 N, as its mass is 2 040 700 kg.

   a Calculate the resultant force on the Space Shuttle at take-off.

   b Calculate the acceleration of the Space Shuttle at take-off.

10 An astronaut is using the manned manoeuvring unit (MMU) to examine solar panels on the ISS. The MMU generates a small thrust force of 60 N, which accelerates the MMU and the astronaut at 0.25 m/s². Calculate the mass of the MMU plus the astronaut. If the astronaut has a mass of 80 kg, what is the mass of the MMU?

Figure 16.9 Astronaut using a manned manoeuvring unit.

Newton's second law and momentum

Newton's second law can be explained and written in a different way using the change in momentum of an object. You will remember that the momentum of an object is equal to the mass of the object multiplied by its velocity. When an object accelerates, it changes its velocity from one value to another. This means that when it accelerates it also changes momentum; the resultant force acting on an accelerating object is equal to the **rate of change of momentum** of the object.

$$\text{resultant force } F\,(\text{N}) \ = \ \frac{\text{change in momentum } \Delta p\ (\text{kg m/s})}{\text{time for the change } t\ (\text{s})}$$

$$F = \frac{\Delta p}{t} = \frac{\Delta mv}{t}$$

Examples

Q An astronaut is using the MMU and their total combined mass is 250 kg. She takes 5 seconds to change velocity from 1.5 m/s to 3.5 m/s. Calculate the initial momentum and final momentum of the astronaut.

A $p_{\text{initial}} = m \times v_{\text{initial}} = 250 \times 1.5 = 375\,\text{kg m/s}$
$p_{\text{final}} = m \times v_{\text{final}} = 250 \times 3.5 = 875\,\text{kg m/s}$

Q Calculate the change in momentum of the astronaut.

A Change in momentum,
$\Delta p = p_{\text{final}} - p_{\text{initial}} = 875 - 375 = 500\,\text{kg m/s}$

Q Calculate the resultant force on the astronaut.

A Resultant force, $F = \dfrac{\Delta p}{t} = \dfrac{500}{5} = 100\,\text{N}$

QUESTIONS

11 During T+200 s and T+300 s of a Space Shuttle launch (i.e. between 200 s and 300 s after launch), the Shuttle (mass = 2 040 700 kg) accelerates from 2600 m/s to 4400 m/s.
   a Calculate the momentum of the Shuttle at:
     i T+200 s
     ii T+300 s
   b Calculate the change in momentum between these times.
   c Calculate the resultant force acting on the Shuttle during this time.
   d During this time, the Shuttle is both gaining altitude and losing mass. Explain how both of these will affect the forces acting on the Shuttle.

12 In preparation for docking with the ISS, a manned Soyuz spacecraft (mass = 7150 kg) changes velocity relative to the ISS from 12.0 m/s to 0.5 m/s.
   a Calculate the change in momentum of the Soyuz.
   b Calculate the resultant decelerating force acting on the Soyuz.
   c The Soyuz has three 'retro-rockets' that are used to decelerate the Soyuz before docking. Explain how these rockets can decelerate the Soyuz.

Touch down!

The Soyuz spacecraft is now the only way that astronauts can travel to and from the ISS. Although the Soyuz is an old design (the first model was built in the 1960s), it is tried and tested.

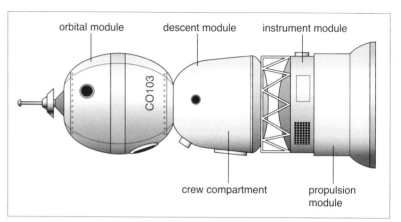

Figure 16.11 Soyuz spacecraft.

The crew return to Earth in the descent module that detaches from the rest of the spacecraft shortly before re-entry.

The descent module starts its free fall through the upper atmosphere with a velocity of over 7800 m/s, as its weight and the effect of the Earth's gravity pull it towards Earth.

As it falls, the force of friction (air resistance), due to the descent module's heatshield colliding with the molecules of gas in the atmosphere, increases dramatically, causing the descent module to decelerate. Eventually the force of the air resistance equals the weight of the descent module: the forces are balanced, equal and opposite, and the module continues to fall, but at a constant (terminal) velocity of about 230 m/s.

Figure 16.10 Soyuz descent module attached to a parachute.

Figure 16.12 Soyuz de-coupling.

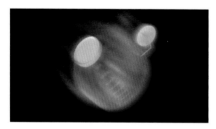

Figure 16.13 Soyuz descent module in upper atmosphere.

Figure 16.14 Soyuz descent module on parachute landing.

At an altitude of 12 km, the parachutes start to deploy, dramatically increasing the air resistance on the descent module, as the area in contact with the air increases. This causes the descent module to decelerate rapidly, eventually reducing its velocity to a slower (terminal) velocity of 7 m/s. One second before touch down, two sets of three small engines on the bottom of the module fire, slowing the descent module further and cushioning the landing on to the steppes of Central Kazakhstan, close to the Baikonur Cosmodrome.

Figure 16.15 The landed descent module and a map of Kazakhstan, showing the location of its landing zone.

PRACTICAL   MAKING A MODEL OF A SOYUZ DESCENT MODULE

This activity helps you with:

★ investigating the terminal velocity of a falling object
★ making a physical model
★ working collaboratively with a partner
★ measuring the behaviour of a falling object
★ analysing the results of an investigation.

You can make a simple model of the Soyuz descent module using a paper cupcake case. You can drop the model from a set height and time how long it takes to fall a set distance. This will not be very accurate; can you think why? There are many things that you can do to investigate the descent of the model – the design engineers of the Soyuz had to reduce the velocity of the descent module as much as possible to reduce the impact of the ground on the cosmonauts. In your investigation you can measure the mean descent velocity by dividing the drop height by the drop time. What could you do to reduce the descent velocity? Change the mass (add cupcake cases)? Add a parachute?

Design, carry out, analyse and evaluate an investigation to design a working model of a Soyuz descent module.

Chapter summary

- Weight is the force of gravity acting on the mass of an object.
- On the surface of Earth, 1 kg of mass has a weight of 10 N; this is called the gravitational field strength g.
- ✓ Newton's first law of motion states that an object at rest stays at rest or an object in motion stays in motion with the same speed and in the same direction unless acted upon by an unbalanced force.
- This can be investigated experimentally, e.g. using an air track and datalogger, where the air cushion reduces friction to a very small value.
- The mass of an object affects how easy or difficult it is to change the movement of that object. Massive bodies have large amounts of inertia, so require a large force to change their motion, or to make them move if they are stationary.
- The momentum of an object is its mass in kg multiplied by its velocity in m/s; that is momentum $= mv$.
- The units of momentum are kg m/s.
- ✓ Newton's second law of motion states that force $=$ mass $\times$ acceleration; that is, the acceleration of an object is directly proportional to the resultant force and inversely proportional to the object's mass.
- In terms of momentum, this becomes force $=$ the rate of change in momentum, or the change in momentum divided by the time taken.
- When an object is falling through the air, initially it accelerates and increases in speed because of the force of gravity acting on it. However, then the force of friction (air resistance) increases, causing the object to decelerate. Eventually the air resistance force equals the weight of the object and it is said to be falling at its terminal (constant) velocity.

The physics of rugby

Figure 17.1 Alun Wyn Jones being lifted in a rugby lineout during the Wales v France match in 2009.

Alun Wyn Jones is lifted in the lineout during the Wales v France match in 2009. Alun is 1.98 m tall (6 ft 6 in) and weighs 118 kg (18 st 10 lbs). The players lifting him effectively lift him through 1.5 m and in doing so have to generate an upwards force between them that is greater than his weight. As they lift him, they do **work**.

Energy and work

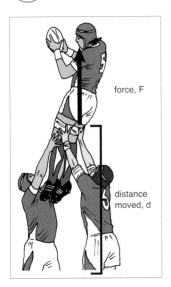

force, F

distance moved, d

Figure 17.2 Showing the distance and the force used in the lineout.

Work is a term in physics used to measure the energy transferred when energy changes from one form to other forms. Energy can transform in lots of different ways, but during a rugby lineout, the players lifting the jumper exert a mechanical force on the player. The energy required to generate this force comes from the chemical energy stored inside the players from their food. Their training programmes make them very efficient at converting this chemical energy into kinetic energy in their muscles. The muscles exert the force moving the jumper upwards through a distance. As work done involves measuring energy transfers, its units are joules, J.

The work done can be determined by the equation:

$$\textbf{work done (J)} = \textbf{force (N)} \times \frac{\textbf{distance moved in the}}{\textbf{direction of the force}} \textbf{(m)}$$

Example

Q Alun Wyn Jones has a mass of 118 kg, giving him a weight of 1180 N. If each player lifting Alun in the lineout exerts half this force (590 N), lifting him through a distance of 1.5 m, calculate the work done by each lifting player.

A work done = force × distance moved = 590 × 1.5 = 885 J

This gives a total work done of (885 × 2) = 1770 J. Putting this into perspective, a small chocolate bar contains about 370 000 J of chemical energy, equivalent to lifting Alun Wyn Jones about 210 times (although not all the chemical energy in the chocolate converts to kinetic energy and gravitational potential energy)!

QUESTIONS

1 What is meant by 'work done'?

2 What are the units of work done?

3 What factors dictate the amount of work done by a player in a lineout lifting a jumper?

4 In a driving maul, players pushing to drive the maul forward typically push with a mean force of 750 N. If the driving maul is pushed 8 m, how much work does a typical player do?

5 During a scrum (Figure 17.3), eight players each push with a mean force of 600 N, moving the scrum 2.5 m.

  a What is the total force exerted by all eight players?

  b Calculate the **total** work done moving the scrum.

Figure 17.3 A scrum.

6 In a head-on driving tackle, a rugby player does 1650 J of work driving the opponent backwards by 3 m. Calculate the force of the tackler.

Figure 17.4 A head-on driving tackle.

7 Calculate the distance that a line-out jumper is lifted if the player lifting the jumper exerts a force of 950 N and does 1520 J of work.

Efficiency

The work done by a player's muscles when lifting, tackling or pushing is always more than the work done on the opponent or their teammate. There is always some energy lost as heat or thermal energy as the muscles do the work. Human muscles are generally only around 20–25% efficient, although elite sportsmen and women may have higher values, up towards 30% efficiency. This means that for every 100 J of chemical energy from a rugby player's food, only about 25 J ends up as mechanical kinetic energy produced by a muscle and 75 J is 'lost' as heat in the muscle cells. This is why people doing sport always get hot and need to cool down by sweating and other body cooling mechanisms.

Examples

During a training programme, rugby players sometimes have to pull a training sled attached to a harness to improve their body strength. The players typically pull the sled with a force of 450 N, for a distance of 20 m.

Q Calculate the work done on the sled.

A Work done on sled = 450 × 20 = 9000 J

Q If the players' muscles are only 25% efficient, calculate the total work done by the players' muscles.

A Work done on sled = 25% of total work done by muscles, so:

$$\text{total work done} \times \frac{25}{100} = 9000$$

$$\text{total work done} = \frac{9000 \times 100}{25} = 36\,000\,\text{J}$$

QUESTIONS

8 What is meant by the efficiency of an energy transfer?

9 Why is heat normally 'wasted' during an energy transfer?

10 Why are muscles only 25% efficient?

11 How do our bodies deal with the heat produced by our muscles when we exercise?

Figure 17.5 Training by pulling a training sled.

HOW MUCH WORK DO YOU DO?

This activity helps you with:
★ working collaboratively with a partner
★ writing a risk assessment
★ measuring forces and distances
★ calculating work done
★ analysing results
★ presenting findings graphically.

You will need to have access to a gym, a set of training weights or other training aids that allow you to exert a force that moves through a distance (such as pilates bands). In this activity you will move forces through measured distances and then calculate the work done by each force. You can also assume that your muscles are only 20% efficient and so you can estimate the amount of chemical energy used by your muscles to generate the work done by the forces.

Risk assessment

Your teacher will give you a blank risk assessment form for you to complete before you do this procedure. You will need to think of all the possible hazards and their associated risks. Ask your teacher to check your risk assessment before you carry out the practical.

Apparatus

* access to gym equipment (or suitable equivalent)
* rulers, tape measures
* large range Newton meters (if available)
* scales calibrated in Newtons (for free weights – if available)

Procedure

1 Complete a suitable risk assessment for this procedure.
2 Identify a suitable exercise using a force that moves through a distance (e.g. any gym machine where a weight is lifted).
3 Set the exercise onto its lowest weight setting and measure and record the mass of the weight that moves and the distance that the weight moves.
4 (Optional) For the same weight setting, measure and record the force that you exert moving the weight (using a suitable Newton meter) and the distance that you move that force.
5 Calculate the weight force of the moving weight using:
weight force (N) = mass (kg) × 10 (N/kg)
6 Calculate the work done moving the weight using:
work done on weight (J) = weight force (N) × distance moved (m)
7 (Optional) Calculate the work done by you moving the weight using:
work done by your force (J) = exerted force (N) × distance moved (m)
8 (Optional) Calculate the efficiency of the machine:

$$\text{efficiency} = \frac{\text{work done moving the weight}}{\text{work done by you}} \times 100\%$$

9 Repeat this procedure for different weight settings on the machine.
10 Repeat on different exercise machines or free exercises.
Suitable non-gym equipment exercises that will produce similar results are:
a press-ups on bathroom scales
b lifting exercise dumb-bells or lab weights
c stretching pilates bands.

Analysing your results

Think how you could display the results of work done and efficiencies (if appropriate) from your experiments. Results like this are best displayed graphically. Produce a graph to show your results. Which exercises required the most work done? Which ones were the most efficient?

Running with a rugby ball – analysing kinetic energy

Figure 17.6 Shane Williams running with the ball.

When objects like rugby players run with a ball, the chemical energy from their food converts to kinetic (movement) energy of their muscles. The moving muscles move the player.

We can calculate the kinetic energy of a moving object using the equation:

$$\text{kinetic energy} = \tfrac{1}{2} \times (\text{mass} \times \text{velocity}^2)$$

$$KE = \tfrac{1}{2} mv^2$$

Example

Q Wales winger Shane Williams can run with a rugby ball with a mean velocity of about 10 m/s. Shane has a mass of 80 kg. When running at 10 m/s, what is Shane's kinetic energy?

A $KE = \tfrac{1}{2} mv^2 = 0.5 \times 80 \times 10^2 = 4000\,\text{J}$

QUESTIONS

12 What is meant by kinetic energy?

13 What does the kinetic energy of a rugby player depend upon?

14 If a rugby player jogs at 5 m/s and then sprints at 10 m/s, she doubles her velocity. By what factor does her kinetic energy increase?

15 At a recent Wales squad training session, the sprinting performance of various players was measured and recorded. Table 17.1 summarises the findings of the fitness director. Copy and complete the table (minus the photos), calculating the maximum kinetic energy of each player.

Table 17.1

Player		Position	Mass (kg)	Maximum sprinting velocity (m/s)	Maximum kinetic energy (J)
Alun Wyn Jones		Lock	118	9.2	
Shane Williams		Winger	80	11.2	
Adam Jones		Prop	127	8.5	
James Hook		Fly-half	93	10.4	

16 A standard (size 5) rugby ball has a mass of 0.44 kg. When kicking from a tee, James Hook can kick the ball with an initial velocity of 24.5 m/s. Calculate the initial kinetic energy of the ball.

This activity helps you with:
★ working as part of a team
★ measuring and recording masses, distances and times
★ considering the range of your measurements
★ calculating velocities and kinetic energies.

When a rugby ball is passed from one player to another you can measure the mean velocity of the pass by dividing the distance between the players by the time of the pass.

Figure 17.7 A rugby pass.

In this activity you will make measurements so that you can calculate the kinetic energy of a passed rugby ball.

Design, carry out and analyse an experiment to determine the range of kinetic energies of a rugby ball when passed over a set distance. You need to make measurements to allow you to determine the highest and the lowest reasonable values (the range).

Think about the equipment that you will need and order this from your teacher or science technician. Do you need to write a risk assessment for this experiment? If so, ask your teacher for a blank risk assessment form.

Kicking a ball – an exercise in gravitational potential energy

Wales fly-half James Hook kicks at goal. When he kicks a rugby ball, he is transferring kinetic energy from his foot into kinetic energy of the ball. As the ball gains height, some of the kinetic energy is transferred into gravitational potential energy. If the ball was kicked vertically upwards (as with a hanging up-and-under), eventually all the kinetic energy of the ball would be converted to gravitational potential energy. With distance kicks, only a proportion of the kinetic energy is converted to gravitational potential energy, as some of the kinetic energy is used up kicking the ball forward.

The gravitational potential energy (PE) of an object such as a rugby ball can be calculated using the equation:

$$\begin{array}{c}\text{gravitational} \\ \text{potential energy}\end{array} = \begin{array}{c}\text{mass } m \\ \text{(kg)}\end{array} \times \begin{array}{c}\text{gravitational} \\ \text{field strength } g \\ \text{(N/kg)}\end{array} \times \begin{array}{c}\text{change in} \\ \text{height } h \text{ (m)}\end{array}$$

$$PE = mgh$$

Figure 17.8 James Hook kicking a ball from the ground.

Example

Q Calculate the gravitational potential energy of a 0.44 kg rugby ball kicked vertically upwards to a height of 20 m. The gravitational field strength g = 10 N/kg.

A PE = mgh = 0.44 × 20 × 10 = 88 J

QUESTIONS

17 What is meant by 'gravitational potential energy'?

18 Apart from the gravitational field strength, what two other factors dictate the gravitational potential energy of a rugby ball?

19 Rugby balls come in three main sizes:
  - Size 3 (ages 6–9), mass = 0.28 kg
  - Size 4 (ages 10–14), mass = 0.38 kg
  - Size 5 (adult), mass = 0.44 kg

  During a media press photo-shoot for a ball sponsor, James Hook kicks all three balls to the same height (35 m). If the gravitational field strength is 10 N/kg, calculate the gravitational potential energy gained by each ball at the top of the kick.

20 Wales hooker Matthew Rees throws the ball into a lineout from an initial height of 2.0 m. The ball gets to a maximum height of 4.2 m, gaining a gravitational potential energy of 9.9 J. If the gravitational field strength is 10 N/kg, calculate the mass of the ball.

When James Hook kicks a ball vertically upwards, he applies a **force** to the ball at the instant of the kick. In doing this, the force moves through a distance and James' foot does **work** on the ball, transferring kinetic energy from his foot into kinetic energy of the ball (and some is lost as heat and sound). The ball's kinetic energy then starts to reduce, as it gains height moving against the pull of gravity – increasing in gravitational potential energy. The ball is doing work against the pull of gravity. Eventually the vertical velocity of the ball gets to zero as it reaches the top of the kick.

The kinetic energy has all been converted to gravitational potential energy. As the ball starts to fall back down again, the opposite happens and gravitational potential energy converts back into kinetic energy. However, at any one time, at any height, the **total** energy of the ball is constant – it is the amount of energy given to it initially by James Hook's foot. So in this case, at any height:

total energy = kinetic energy + gravitational potential energy

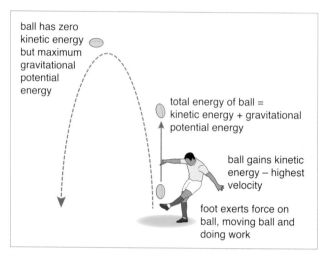

Figure 17.9 A rugby player kicking a ball.

GRAVITATIONAL POTENTIAL ENERGY AND THE RUGBY LINEOUT

You will take part in a rugby lineout. You need one player (in this case, someone light, with a lower mass) to be the jumper, two players to lift the jumper round the waist, one person to throw the ball in to the jumper from about 5 m away, and one person to measure the height that the jumper jumps through and the height that the ball is caught.

This activity helps you with:
★ working as part of a team
★ measuring heights and masses
★ calculating gravitational potential energies.

Apparatus
* rugby ball
* gym mats or crash mats
* 4 × wooden metre rulers, taped together to make a long ruler
* electronic balance to measure the mass of the rugby ball
* bathroom scales to measure the mass of the jumper
* access to a gym

Risk assessment

Your teacher will give you a risk assessment for this activity, but the person being lifted must be reasonably agile and the two people lifting must be capable of lifting the jumper under control. Your teacher will show you how to lift the jumper safely, and you must do this activity on gym mats or crash mats.

Procedure
1 Arrange yourselves into teams of 5 or 6.
2 The lightest person is the jumper. Measure and record the mass of the jumper in kg using the bathroom scales.

Figure 17.10 Rugby lineout.

PRACTICAL *contd.*

3 Two people must practise lifting the jumper. Measure and record the height jumped by the jumper (you could measure the height difference of the jumper's shoulders).

4 Measure and record the mass of the rugby ball in kg.

5 Measure the height of the ball before it is thrown.

6 When the thrower throws the ball to the jumper, the person measuring the height holds the long ruler near to the jumper and estimates and records the height reached by the ball at the catch height.

7 Calculate the extra height gained by the ball.

8 Repeat this procedure twice more and calculate mean values for each measurement.

9 Calculate the mean gravitational potential energy gained by the jumper and the ball.

10 There are many alternatives to this activity. For example, you could use almost any ball sport, particularly ones played in a gym such as basketball, badminton and netball. If you have time, compare the gravitational potential energies gained by a range of different balls in sport.

Discussion Point

Explain why using an estimate is sometimes acceptable in science. Can you think of other situations where you use estimates?

Scrummaging – a case study in Newton's third law

Figure 17.11 A rugby scrum.

During a scrum, two very large forces come into contact. If we consider a static (non-moving) scrum, then we know that the force exerted by one set of forwards must be equal and opposite to the force exerted by the other set. The forces act as a **pair**.

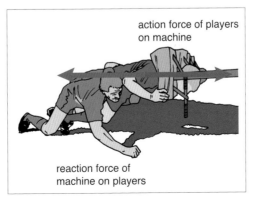

action force of players on machine

reaction force of machine on players

Figure 17.12 Players scrummaging against a scrum-machine.

It is easier to see the forces acting in a scrum when the players are using a scrum-machine.

If the machine is stationary, then the resultant force due to the interaction of all the forces acting on the scrummaging machine must be zero. The force exerted **by the players** on the machine is equal and opposite to the force exerted **on the players** by the machine. The forces act in pairs: one (from the players) is called the **action** force and one (from the machine) is called the **reaction** force; together they form an **interaction pair**.

Forces always act in pairs. Some forces (like those involved with scrummaging) are **contact** forces: two objects must come into contact with each other to exert the force. Other forces are **action at a distance** forces, such as gravity, or the forces exerted by electric and magnetic fields. Isaac Newton first realised that forces act in pairs and he summarised this in his **third law of motion**, first published in 1687:

> *'In an interaction between two objects, A and B, the force exerted by body A on body B is equal and oppositely directed to the force exerted by body B on body A.'*

> Or in other words: *'For every action force, there is an equal and opposite reaction force.'*

When using Newton's Third Law, the following points need to be understood:

1. The two forces in an interaction pair act on different objects.
2. The two forces are equal in size, but act in opposite directions.
3. The two forces are always the same type, for example contact forces or gravitational forces.

On the scrum-machine, there are lots of other force interaction pairs (everywhere where there are two bodies in contact with each other), but there are 16 very important pairs – between each player's feet and the ground.

Figure 17.13 Close-up of scrum, showing interaction between feet and ground.

The foot of the player exerts a backwards force on the ground. The ground exerts a forwards force on the foot, due to friction. The two are equal and opposite and the foot stays stationary.

QUESTIONS

21 What is Newton's third law?

22 What are the names of the two forces in an interaction pair?

23 What are the two main types of force?

24 Explain why a rugby player involved with pushing in a maul would only fall on to the ground if she slipped or if the maul collapsed.

25 Look at the following diagrams. Sketch each diagram and label the force interaction pairs in each case.

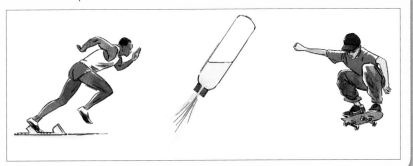

Chapter summary

○ Work is done when energy is transferred from one form to another.

○ The unit of work is the joule, J.

○ The work done can be calculated by using the equation:
work done (J) = force used (N) × distance moved in the direction of the force (m)

○ There is always a proportion of energy lost as heat or sound when energy is transferred from one form to another. For example human muscles are about 25% efficient so about 75% of the energy used by the muscle cells becomes heat rather than kinetic energy.

○ The kinetic energy (KE) of a moving object can be calculated using the equation: $KE = \frac{1}{2} mv^2$.

○ For objects moving through the air in an upwards direction, their kinetic energy will gradually change to gravitational potential energy as the object does work against gravity. The object will start to slow down as it has less kinetic energy.

○ Gravitational potential energy (PE) can be found using the equation:
PE = mass (kg) × gravitational strength g (N/kg) × change in height (m)

○ When all the kinetic energy of the object has converted to gravitational potential energy, the vertical velocity of the object is then zero, and the object starts to fall down again as the potential energy starts to convert back to kinetic energy.

○ At any point in the object's movement, the total energy remains constant as this is the sum of the kinetic energy plus the potential energy.

○ Newton's third law states: *'In an interaction between two objects, A and B, the force exerted by body A on body B is equal and oppositely directed to the force exerted by body B on body A'.*

○ Together the action force and the reaction force make an interaction pair.

○ Forces may be 'contact' forces, where objects need to come into contact with each other to exert the force, or they may be 'action at a distance' forces such as gravity or electromagnetic forces.

Cars, the Highway Code and collisions

Figure 18.1 A motorway crash.

The Highway Code has a lot to say about stopping safely. If you understand the 'mechanics' of stopping when you are learning to drive, you are less likely to have an accident. This is why there are questions on stopping distances in the driving theory test. So what does the Highway Code have to say, and what is the physics behind stopping safely?

We already know that moving objects such as cars and rugby players (Chapter 17) have kinetic energy. We also know that kinetic energy depends on mass and velocity where:

$$KE = \tfrac{1}{2}mv^2$$

So heavy lorries have more kinetic energy than cars travelling at the same velocity, and vehicles moving faster have more kinetic energy than slower vehicles. In fact, as you can see from the equation, if you double the velocity of an object, then the kinetic energy is four times as much (as $2^2 = 4$)!

When a driver wants to stop a car, he or she has to rely on the friction in the brakes and the friction between the tyre and road surface to do work to bring the car to rest. Remember from Chapter 17 that work is done when a force moves through a distance. In the case of car brakes, the kinetic energy is converted into heat (absorbed by the brake pads).

Total stopping distance of a vehicle

Vehicles do not stop instantaneously – there is a time delay between the driver seeing the potential hazard, and the vehicle stopping. During this time, the vehicle is still travelling at speed so the car travels through a distance. The **total stopping distance** of a vehicle is made up of the thinking distance and the braking distance.

The **thinking distance** is the distance that the vehicle travels whilst the driver sees the hazard, thinks about braking and then actually reacts to put the brakes on.

The **braking distance** is the distance that the vehicle moves while the brakes are being applied. During the time that the brakes are being applied, the vehicle is decelerating to 0 m/s.

total stopping distance = thinking distance + braking distance

Thinking distance depends on several different factors including:

- The velocity of the car – the higher the velocity, the further the car will travel whilst the driver is thinking about applying the brakes (distance = velocity × time).
- The **reaction time** of the driver. This is normally about 0.7 s. Reaction times depend on lots of different factors but it is substantially increased if the driver has been drinking alcohol or taking drugs – even some common cold remedies can cause drowsiness. Many accidents are also caused by tired drivers – you may have seen signs on the motorway like the one in Figure 18.2.
- The driver may be distracted, in particular by children in the back of the car.
- The driver may have been using a mobile phone; even hands-free sets seriously affect thinking distances. Other similar distractions could include fiddling with the car radio/CD/mp3, fiddling with the SatNav, drinking coffee etc.

Discussion Point

It is now illegal to use a hand-held mobile phone while driving. However, some people still do use hand-held mobile phones and drive at the same time. Why do you think they do this?

Figure 18.2 Motorway sign urging tired drivers to have a rest.

The braking distance also depends on several factors. These include:

- The velocity of the car. Remember, the kinetic energy of a vehicle depends on the square of its velocity – double the velocity, quadruple the kinetic energy.
- The mass of the car. The greater the mass, the greater the kinetic energy.
- The condition of the **brakes**. Excess wear or contamination with oil and grease will seriously affect the brakes. Oil and grease on the discs of the brakes will act as a lubricant, reducing the friction and increasing the braking distance.

- The condition of the surface of the **tyres**. They must have at least 1.6 mm of tread (groove) over 75% of the width of the tyre. The grooves clear away the water on a wet road. With smooth tyres and a wet road, a thin layer of water builds up between the road and the tyre, reducing the friction. This can lead to a dangerous condition known as aquaplaning.
- The condition of the **road surface**. Road surfaces such as gravel, or surfaces covered with sand or dust will reduce the friction between the tyres and the road and so increase the braking distance.
- The **weather**. Any water, ice or snow between the tyres and the road surface will act as a lubricant, reducing friction and increasing the braking distance.

The diagram below is adapted from the Highway Code. It shows how thinking distance, stopping distance and total stopping distance all increase with vehicle velocity. Reducing velocity can prevent accidents and save lives, because the total stopping distance is reduced.

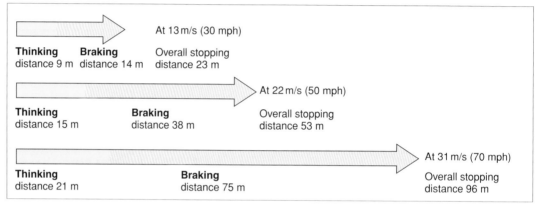

Figure 18.3 Thinking and stopping distances.

QUESTIONS

1 For a vehicle, what is the:
   a thinking distance
   b braking distance
   c total stopping distance?
2 State and explain **two** factors that affect the thinking distance of a stopping car.
3 Do you think that smoking whilst driving a car affects the total stopping distance? Explain your answer.
4 Increased tyre tread greatly reduces the braking distance of a car. Why do you think that cars are not all fitted with thick, chunky, off-road tyres with huge treads?

PRESENTING AND ANALYSING DATA FROM THE HIGHWAY CODE

This activity helps you with:
★ presenting data graphically
★ looking for patterns in graphical data.

The data in Table 18.1 shows the velocities, thinking distances, braking distances and total stopping distances taken from the Highway Code.

Table 18.1 Stopping distances at different velocities (taken from the Highway Code).

Velocity (m/s)	Velocity (mph)	Thinking distance (m)	Braking distance (m)	Total stopping distance (m)
0	0	0	0	0
9	20	6	6	12
13	30	9	14	23
18	40	12	24	36
22	50	15	38	53
27	60	18	55	73
31	70	21	75	96

Draw a graph of this data, with the velocity (m/s) on the x-axis, and stopping distances on the y-axis. You will need to plot three sets of data on the same graph with a suitable key. As we generally use mph as our unit of velocity when driving, draw labelled vertical lines on your graphs to illustrate these velocities.

Questions
The following questions are about analysing your stopping distance graph.
1 What are the:
   a thinking distance at 15 m/s?
   b braking distance at 55 **mph**?
   c total stopping distance at 29 m/s?
2 A car has a total stopping distance of 16 m. What is the car's velocity?
3 There is a direct link between thinking distance and velocity. What pattern is shown on the thinking distance versus velocity graph?
4 Calculate the reaction time of a driver at 50 mph.
5 The braking distance at 9 m/s is 6 m. What is the braking distance at double this velocity? How is the braking distance at double the velocity related to the braking distance at 9 m/s?
6 Describe the shape of the braking distance graph. How do you think that it is calculated?
7 Why does the driving theory test ask questions about total stopping distance?
8 Find out what the Highway Code has to say about drinking alcohol and driving.

Is there such a thing as a 'safe speed'?

All roads are generally safe...the thing that can make them dangerous is motorists and lorry drivers! Motorways are better roads because the lanes are wide, the road surface is generally very good and they are usually straight. As a result traffic can travel fast on motorways. The Highway Code states that the speed limit for cars and motorcycles on a motorway is 70 mph (or 31 m/s); for cars towing caravans or trailers and heavy goods vehicles, the speed limit is 60 mph (or 27 m/s). In town centres, where the traffic is heavy and there are lots of people crossing roads, with the added hazards of parked cars, schools, etc., the speed limit is substantially lower, often set at 30 mph (13 m/s) for all vehicles. Although the speed limit in these built-up areas may be 30 mph, this does not mean that it is necessarily safe to travel at 30 mph. Drivers should always adjust their speed to the road conditions, the amount of traffic, pedestrians, bikes and the weather.

Not all drivers keep to the speed limit. To enforce the law, local authorities and the police use speed cameras and other 'traffic calming' measures. Static speed cameras take two flash photographs of a speeding vehicle. White marks on the road enable police to see how far the car has travelled in the time between the flashes. From this they can work out the driver's velocity.

The police can also use mobile 'speed guns', which are devices that fire pulses of an infra-red laser beam at a speeding car. The car reflects the infra-red pulses and these are detected again by the gun. The computer in the gun measures and records the time between infra-red pulses being emitted and received. From this it can work out the instantaneous velocity of the car.

Figure 18.4 Static 'gatso-type' speed camera.

Figure 18.5 Police using mobile speed gun.

Some drivers speed up after passing a camera. To stop this dangerous practice some cameras are connected to a computer which records the number plate of every passing vehicle. A second camera, which may be some miles further down the road, records the number plates again. The computer uses the time interval and distance between the two cameras to calculate mean velocity of the vehicles.

Other 'traffic calming' measures include the following.

- 'Speed bumps' are raised humps across the road, or individual mounds on the road. Motorists must slow down before they drive over them, or risk damage to their car. Sometimes people who live close to speed bumps complain about the noise of traffic going over the bumps.

Figure 18.6 Speed bumps.

- Road width restrictions – these can be set up where one half of the road is blocked off for a short distance. Traffic on one side has to stop if there is oncoming traffic.

Figure 18.7 Road width restrictions.

QUESTIONS

5 Why do we have national speed limits in the UK?

6 What are the national speed limits on:

  a a motorway?

  b a road in a busy town centre?

7 Describe **one** road safety measure used to reduce speed in your area. Explain whether you think that the road safety measure has in fact improved road safety.

8 In your opinion, which is the most dangerous road near where you live or your school? How would you go about improving road safety on that road?

What do you think about this article? Are speed cameras a good idea or a bad idea? How could you use the data in the article to create a chart in support of speed cameras?

SPEED CAMERAS SWITCHED ON AGAIN

Speed cameras in one county which were switched off last year due to spending cuts have been switched on again. Thames Valley Police said 72 fixed camera sites and 89 mobile sites in Oxfordshire are resuming operations. They were switched off on August 1 2010 after Oxfordshire County Council cut the authority's road safety grant. Superintendent Rob Povey, head of roads policing for Thames Valley, said: 'We think this is important because we know that speed kills and speed is dangerous. We have shown in Oxfordshire that speed has increased through monitoring limits and we have noticed an increase in fatalities and the number of people seriously injured in 2010. We know that speed enforcement does work as a deterrent to motorists.'

Data released by Thames Valley Police shows in the six months after they were switched off, 83 people were injured in 62 accidents at the site of fixed cameras. The figure for the same period the year before (August 2009 to January 2010) was 68 injuries in 60 accidents. Across Oxford, 18 people were killed in road traffic accidents in the period, compared with 12 people the year before. The number of people seriously injured rose by 19 to 179. Mr Povey said the money for switching on the cameras came from cutting back office costs and from funding diverted from speed awareness courses. Professor Stephen Glaister, director of the RAC Foundation, said that speed cameras are 'controversial' but their research suggested they prevent 800 fatalities and serious injuries each year.

The safest car in the world?

Car manufacturers are always improving and adding safety features to reduce injuries in collisions – both to car occupants and pedestrians. The Euro NCAP (the European body that tests car safety) rating is now used as a marketing device for car manufacturers, particularly when targeting marketing towards family cars. This marketing is seen as critical by Euro NCAP, with manufacturers realising that there is money to be made by manufacturing cars with improved safety. One of the factors that affects the amount of damage to drivers and passengers in a car crash is the rapid change of momentum that occurs when the car crashes. If you are in a car that suddenly slows down, rapidly decreasing your momentum, your **motion** keeps you moving forward until a force acts to change your velocity (remember Newton's first law from Chapter 16). This could be the force between your head and the windscreen. You will also remember Newton's second law which states:

$$\text{force (N)} = \frac{\text{change in momentum (kg m/s)}}{\text{time for change (s)}} = \frac{\Delta mv}{t}$$

If you decrease your momentum quickly there will be a large force on your body. Anything that increases the time taken for the collision will mean that you are less likely to be injured as the rate of change of momentum will be less and thus so will the force. The trick in car safety design is to engineer systems within the car that will increase the time for a collision and yet keep the passengers safe inside a strong passenger compartment.

Figure 18.8 Car with crumpled crumple zone.

Car makers design their cars so that they will collapse gradually on impact – significantly increasing the time of the collision and substantially reducing the force on the occupants. These features are called **crumple zones**. There is one at the front and one at the rear of the car. The front crumple zone allows the bonnet and the engine to 'concertina' up on itself, as it is gradually pushed back into the car along extremely stiff rails. This increases the collision time and also takes a great deal of the kinetic energy out of the crash, deforming the front end of the car.

QUESTIONS

9 What is a crumple zone?
10 How do crumple zones reduce the force on the occupants of a car during a crash?
11 Why is it important that cars are designed with front **and** rear crumple zones?

PRACTICAL DESIGNING AND TESTING CRUMPLE ZONES

This activity helps you with:
★ making a model of a crumple zone
★ designing and testing different crumple zone ideas.

Crumple zones come in many different forms. You can model crumple zones in a variety of different ways. Your teacher will demonstrate one such model.

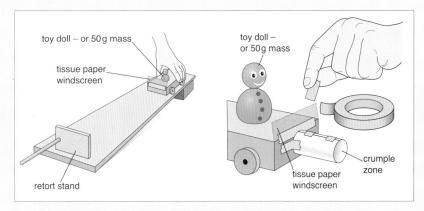

Figure 18.9 Apparatus to show the effect of a car crumple zone.

Apparatus
* dynamics trolley
* assorted materials to make different designs of crumple zone
* plasticine block and match 'decelerometer' (see Figure 18.10)
* ramp

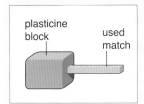

Figure 18.10

⚠ Risk assessment

Your teacher will give you a risk assessment for this practical.

Procedure
1 You can compare the effect of different crumple zones by using a simple plasticine-match decelerometer. Fix the plasticine to the front of the dynamics trolley with sticky tape; as the trolley crashes, the match will be forced into the plasticine block. Measuring the amount that the match is pushed into the plasticine gives a comparison of the force during the collision. The lower the force, the better your design of crumple zone.
2 Use the selection of materials to design different crumple zone designs that will fit on the front of the dynamics trolley. Remember to make it a fair test by having them all the same width so that they all trigger the decelerometer at the same time.
3 Which system was best? Why do you think it was best?

Is there such a thing as a 'safe speed'?

The central part of a car is extremely strong and does not crumple. This is called the **safety cage**, and it is designed to protect all the occupants in the event of a collision. The safety cage prevents the crumple zones from impacting inwards towards the passengers and they now all have 'side-impact' bars fitted that make the crumple zone very strong against side impacts (one of the most common forms of collision).

Figure 18.11 A 'skeleton' car safety cage.

QUESTIONS

12 Why does a safety cage need to be strong?

13 Where do you think the safety cage is in your family car?

14 Why are most new cars fitted with side-impact bars?

15 What materials do you think safety cages are made from?

Seat belts and airbags

Safety seat belts and airbags have made a dramatic improvement to our chances of survival in a crash.

Figure 18.12 Crash test dummy wearing a safety belt during a collision and hitting an airbag during a collision.

Seat belts and airbags work in a similar way to crumple zones. They are designed to increase the time of the collision for the occupants of the car. During a crash, the seat belt restrains you into your seat, preventing you (if you are in the front seats) from hitting the steering wheel, dashboard or windscreen, or in the case of the rear seat passengers, the front seats. However, the seat belt would also cause you a considerable amount of damage if it didn't stretch during the impact. Seat belts are made from a webbing type material that stretches in a controlled way during a collision.

Discussion Points

1 Use the internet to find out the statistics on seat belt and airbag safety. Is it possible to put any numbers on how many lives have been saved by these two car safety systems?

2 Car manufacturers are now turning their attention to making cars safer for pedestrians during collisions. Use the internet to find out how some of the major car manufacturers are doing this. Why do you think that it has taken so long for manufacturers to start really addressing the problems of pedestrian safety?

The stretchy material increases the time of the collision, greatly reducing the rate of change of momentum and therefore the force that acts on you. Because the seat belts stretch, and don't return to their original shape, they have to be replaced after a collision in which they have been activated. Some cars have seat belt pre-tensioners. They sense the impact (using electronic deceleration sensors in the engine cavity) and tighten the belt a little to reduce the effect of the collision. Airbags inflate automatically on impact – they are usually connected to the same sensors as the seat belt pre-tensioners. When the car occupants' heads hit the airbags, the bags deflate slowly as the force of impact pushes some of the gas out. The airbag increases the time it takes for the person's head to slow down and stop, so the force acting on the head is not as great.

QUESTIONS

16 How does a seat belt prevent you from serious injury in a crash?

17 Why are seat belts made from a webbing type material?

18 Why is it very important that passengers in the rear of the car wear seat belts?

19 Why do some cars have seat belt pre-tensioners? Why do they reduce the risk of serious injury even further?

20 How do airbags work?

21 Why is an airbag designed to increase the collision time between a driver's head and the steering wheel?

22 Modern cars are fitted with an array of different airbags – find out where the airbags are on your car. Why are the airbags positioned there?

Chapter summary

- The total stopping distance of a vehicle is the sum of the thinking distance and the braking distance.
- The factors which affect these distances are the velocity of the car, the reaction time of the driver, the mass of the car, the condition of the vehicle's brakes and tyres, the condition of the road surface and the weather conditions.
- In the UK, the speed limit for cars on motorways is 70 mph. For cars towing caravans and heavy goods vehicles it is 60 mph.
- In built-up or heavily pedestrianised areas it may be reduced to 20 or 30 mph.
- Traffic cameras are connected to computers that can calculate the velocity of passing vehicles to see if they are keeping to the speed limit.
- Safety features in cars reduce the numbers of injuries and deaths when cars are involved in accidents. These include safety belts and airbags, and crumple zones and safety cages. All of these features act by increasing the time taken for the collision to take place, so reducing the rate of change of momentum of the car passengers and thus the force acting on them.

Using radioactive decay

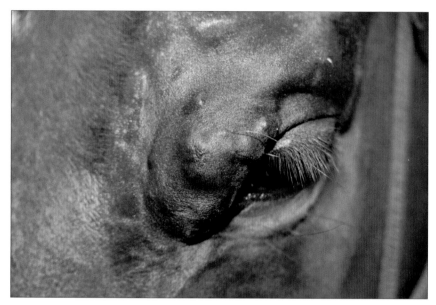

Figure 19.1 A horse suffering from an eye sarcoid.

The horse in the picture is suffering from a particular type of growth around the eye called a sarcoid. Sarcoids are benign tumours (skin conditions where the skin cells in a particular area become inflamed) and they are difficult to treat surgically when they appear around the eye – veterinary surgeons are unwilling to operate on these growths for fear of blinding the horse. Another way to treat these growths, however, is to kill the cells using radiation from a radioactive source. You will remember that alpha (α), beta (β) and gamma (γ) are forms of ionising radiation that can kill body tissues – the energy of the radiation can cause atoms in the cell to ionise, so killing (or mutating) them in the process. When treating sarcoids, veterinary surgeons use β radiation, because it is ionising and penetrates only a short way into the body. The β particles emitted by a source, usually in the form of a wire, kill the sarcoid growth but do not penetrate much further than 3 or 4 cm into the body, causing minimal damage around the growth. The radioactive isotope chosen for this procedure is the element iridium-192, because iridium-192 has a half-life of 74 days. This means that after 74 days the activity of the radioactive source has halved in this time and after about 370 days (about five half-lives), the activity will have dropped to background levels and the source will no longer be considered active. This gives enough time for the iridium-192 to be transferred from the nuclear reactor where it is made, to the surgeon for insertion into the sarcoid for 4 to 14 days, and then returned to the reactor.

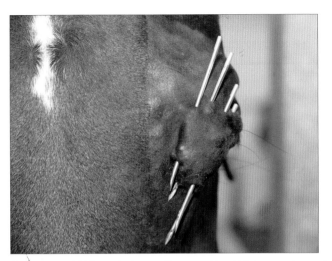

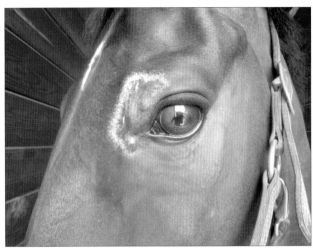

Figure 19.2 a) Iridium wire inserted into sarcoid and b) the same horse after treatment.

Radioactive decay

Figure 19.3 Henri Becquerel.

Radioactive decay is a random event, governed by the laws of probability. If you have a collection of 120 radioactive atoms, you cannot say for definite which atoms will decay in a given time, in the same way that you cannot state for definite if you throw 120 dice which ones will come up with a six. What you can say is that if you throw 120 dice, the probability is that 1 in 6 will come up with a six, i.e. you expect 20 dice to show a six. Any atom of a radioactive isotope has the same chance as any other of decaying. This can be measured using a number known as the **half-life**. This is the **time** that it will take for **half** the number of atoms in any sample to decay. For any one type of atom, this is constant. Isotopes with very long half-lives remain radioactive for a very long time, whereas isotopes with very short half-lives only remain radioactive for fractions of seconds.

The unit of radioactive activity is the becquerel, Bq, named in honour of Henri Becquerel, who 'discovered' radioactivity in 1896. An activity of 1 Bq is equivalent to 1 radioactive decay per second, which is quite a low value. A 0.5 g iridium-192 wire will have a total activity of $160\,000\,000\,000\,000\,\text{Bq}$ $(160 \times 10^{12}\,\text{Bq})$!
(A Geiger counter will measure appreciably smaller activities than this because it only measures the small proportion of the β particles emitted in the direction of the Geiger counter, a short distance away from the source.)

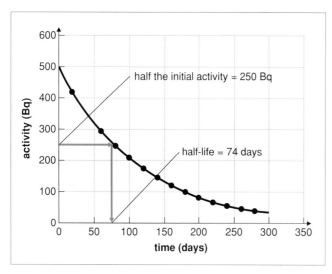

Figure 19.4 Radioactive decay graph of iridium-192.

The radioactive decay graph of iridium-192 is shown in Figure 19.4. The graph shows how the activity of a sample of iridium-192 varies with time.

You can see from the graph that the initial activity of the sample of iridium-192 is 500 Bq. We can use the graph to measure the half-life of the iridium-192. Half-life is defined as the time taken for the activity to halve, in this case the time it takes for the activity to go down to $\frac{500}{2} = 250$ Bq. If we use the graph as shown to measure the time that this takes, it turns out to be 74 days.

All radioactive isotopes have decay graphs that look like this (it's actually a shape called exponential decay). The only difference between different radioactive isotopes is that the ranges on the axes are changed. For radioactive isotopes such as uranium-238, with a half-life of 4.47 billion years, the time axis would need to go up to about 20 billion years! In comparison, technetium-99, an isotope routinely used in bone scans, has a half-life of 6 hours, and would have a time axis that would go up to about 30 hours.

QUESTIONS

1 What are the three types of radioactive decay?
2 What can ionising radiation do to living cells?
3 What is the half-life of a radioactive isotope?
4 After how many half-lives will the activity of a radioactive sample be about the same as natural background activity?
5 Why is iridium-192 chosen to treat eye sarcoids on horses?
6 How long will it take a sample of iridium-192 with an initial activity of 1200 Bq to reach an activity of 75 Bq? [Remember, the half-life of Ir-192 is 74 days.]
7 A sample of iridium-192 has an activity of 215 Bq, 296 days after it was removed from the nuclear reactor that made it.
  a How many half-lives have elapsed in 296 days?
  b What was the initial activity of the sample?
8 Table 19.1 shows the radioactive decay of a sample of iodine-131, a radioactive isotope sometimes used to treat thyroid gland problems.
  a Plot a graph of activity (*y*-axis) against time (*x*-axis).
  b Draw a best-fit line (curve) through your points.
  c Use your graph to measure the half-life of iodine-131.

Table 19.1

Time (days)	0	4	8	12	16	20	24	28	32
Activity (Bq)	800	566	400	283	200	141	100	71	50

THE RADIOACTIVE DECAY OF PROTACTINIUM-234

An excellent radioactive decay simulation can be downloaded from: http://visualsimulations.co.uk/software.php?program=radiationlab

Protactinium-234 is a β emitter, with a half-life of just over 1 minute. Your teacher may show you a special 'protactinium generator' that can be used in the laboratory to produce enough protactinium to measure its decay and determine its half-life.

 Risk assessment

Your teacher will give you a risk assessment for this activity. You are not allowed to do this experiment yourself. It can only be demonstrated to you.

Apparatus
* Geiger counter
* protactinium generator
* stop clock

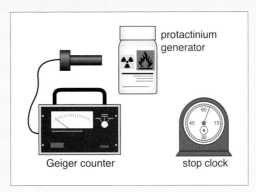

Figure 19.5 Pa-234 decay experiment.

Procedure
1 Your teacher will set up all the necessary apparatus, including the protactinium generator.
2 Your teacher will show you a suitable table for you to record the results of this experiment.
3 The stop clock will be started and the Geiger counter used to measure the activity of the source at t = 0 s (there are several ways of doing this that depend on what type of Geiger counter your teacher is using so they will explain the exact method to you).
4 Measure and record the activity of the protactinium generator every 15 s for about 5 minutes (300 s), using an appropriate table.
5 Plot a radioactive decay curve graph from your results and use your graph to measure the half-life of protactinium-234.
6 You can do a computer simulation of this experiment yourself. Use the link given at the start of the practical to download the (free) simulation and perform the experiment. You will need to use the 'key' at the bottom of the screen to 'collect' the protactinium source from the 'radiation cupboard'.

Carbon dating

Carbon-14 is a naturally occurring radioactive isotope of carbon. Only about 1 atom in every 10 000 000 000 carbon atoms is an atom of carbon-14, however. Carbon-14 is radioactive, emitting β particles with a half-life of 5730 years. Carbon-14 is a very important isotope as it can be used to date organic objects up to about 60 000 years old, so this makes it very useful for dating early human objects as it corresponds to about the time when our early *Homo sapiens* ancestors started to migrate out of Africa.

All living things contain carbon. The ratio of non-radioactive carbon-12 atoms to radioactive carbon-14 atoms in living material is known very precisely – it depends on the composition of the carbon dioxide in the atmosphere. When an organic living creature or plant dies, the ratio of carbon-12 to carbon-14 starts to change as the carbon-14 decays and no more fresh carbon-14 is added, as photosynthesis and/or respiration is no longer carried out by the dead creature or plant. By measuring the ratio of carbon-12 to carbon-14 in a dead organic object, it is possible to use the half-life of carbon-14 to work backwards to find out when the ratio was the same as it is in living organisms now. A graph similar to the one in Figure 19.6 can be used to measure the percentage of C-14 remaining compared with a living sample.

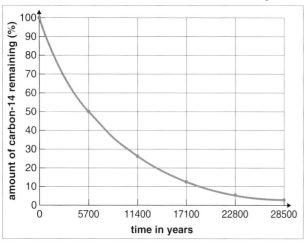

Figure 19.6 Graph of radioactive decay of C-14.

Discussion Point

There is much debate about the authenticity of the Turin Shroud. Recent scientific studies have found that while there is no evidence of any scientific forgery, and the origin of the image on the shroud is still unknown, there is also a suggestion that the samples of the cloth examined in 1988 are not representative of the whole shroud. What happens in this case? The carbon dating data indicates the shroud is a medieval artefact. Is it possible to prove one way or another that the shroud is real, or a very, very elaborate and clever hoax?

QUESTIONS

9   What is carbon dating?

10 Why do you think that dating dead organic materials over 60 000 years old is almost impossible using carbon dating?

11 The Turin Shroud is a holy relic, reputedly the shroud used to wrap Jesus in after his crucifixion. The shroud appears to have the image of a man 'etched' on one side of the cloth. In 1988, three independent carbon-dating laboratories analysed fibres taken from the shroud and discovered that the samples studied contained just over 90% of the original amount of carbon-14. Use the carbon dating graph in Figure 19.6 to estimate the age of the Turin Shroud.

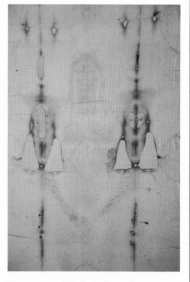

Figure 19.7 The Turin Shroud.

TASK — USING RADIOACTIVE MATERIALS

Radioactive materials are used in a wide variety of different situations. To fully understand each use we need to re-examine the properties of the different forms of radioactive decay.

This activity helps you with:
★ examining data about radioactive isotopes
★ reading about uses of radioactivity and deciding which isotopes might be best to use for them.

Table 19.2 Properties of the different forms of radioactive decay.

Characteristic	Alpha, α	Beta, β	Gamma, γ
Nature (what is it?)	Two protons and two neutrons, identical to a helium nucleus ejected from a nucleus	An electron emitted from a nucleus when a neutron decays into a proton and an electron	An electromagnetic ray emitted from the nucleus when the protons and neutrons re-arrange themselves
Nuclear symbol	$^{4}_{2}He$	$^{0}_{-1}e$	γ
Graphic			
Penetration (how far they will penetrate into different materials)	A few cm of air, sheet of paper or thin layer of skin	A few mm of aluminium or perspex, several cm of flesh, or about 15 cm in air	Reduced (but not completely) absorbed by several cm of lead
Ionising power	Very high as they have a high (+2) charge	Medium – negatively (−1) charged	Low – uncharged
Biological effect	Very high – cause about 20 times more damage than β or γ	Medium	Low
Commonly available radioactive elements (and half-life)	Polonium-210 (138 days) Americium-241 (432 years)	Strontium-90 (28.5 years) Thallium-204 (3.78 years) Carbon-14 (5730 years) Iridium-192 (74 days) Iodine-131 (8 days)	Barium-133 (10.7 years) Cadmium-109 (453 days) Cobalt-57 (270 days) Cobalt-60 (5.27 years) Europium-152 (13.5 years) Manganese-54 (312 days) Sodium-22 (2.6 years) Zinc-65 (244 days) Technetium-99 (6.01 hours)

Use the data in Table 19.2 to decide which radioactive element might be best for use in the following applications.

continued...

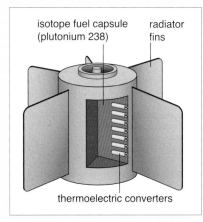

isotope fuel capsule (plutonium 238)   radiator fins

thermoelectric converters

Figure 19.8 A radioisotope thermoelectric generator.

Radioisotope thermoelectric generators

A radioisotope thermoelectric generator (RTG) is a very simple device. It gets hot and generates electricity (no moving parts).

When radioactive elements decay they can produce a large amount of heat. This heat can then be converted directly into electricity using a thermopile (a sandwich of different materials that generate a voltage when heated). RTGs have mainly been used in unmanned space-probes but they are also commonly used in remote mid-ocean navigation buoys and very remote lighthouses.

Questions

1 Which radioactive element from the table would you use for an RTG? Explain your answer.
2 Why do you think that RTGs are only used as the power supply on un-manned devices?

Medical uses

Radio-imaging

Radioactive tracers are used a great deal in medicine. They can check that the internal organs of the body are working properly. The patient swallows or is injected with a radioactive substance. As it decays, the radiation is detected outside the body with a sensitive Geiger counter that can be scanned over or around the patient creating a 2D or 3D 'radio-image'. Many radioactive tracer elements are chemically attached to molecules that accumulate in certain parts of the body (they are targeted at specific organs or bones). The radioactive element must have a very short half-life. Any radioactivity must decay quickly so that there is little chance of it damaging healthy cells.

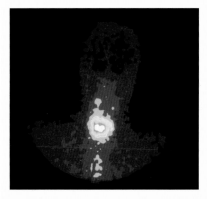

Figure 19.9 Scan of person injected with iodine-131; this has shown that the patient has an enlarged thyroid gland.

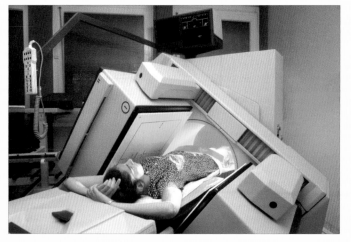

Figure 19.10 Gamma camera in operation.

Using a radioactive tracer can:
- detect problems with the digestive system
- detect problems with the heart and blood vessels
- detect bone cancers
- detect problems with kidneys
- find and image underactive thyroid glands
- be used in research to find causes and cures for diseases such as cancer, AIDS and Alzheimer's disease.

TASK *contd.*

Questions

3 Which radioactive elements would be suitable for use as a radioactive tracer? Explain your answer.

4 Why is it important that the radioactive tracer that is used has a very short half-life?

Radiotherapy

Radiotherapy is another medical use of radioisotopes, but it is different from radio-imaging because the radiation produced by a source is specifically chosen to kill cells. The treatment of eye sarcoids in horses is one type of radiotherapy. The half-lives and penetrating powers of the radioactive isotopes used in radiotherapy must be chosen very carefully to avoid damaging healthy cells. Radiotherapy is usually used to treat tumours, including both cancerous and benign ones. There are three types of radiotherapy:

● External beam radiotherapy, where a beam of γ rays is focused on a particular part of the body.

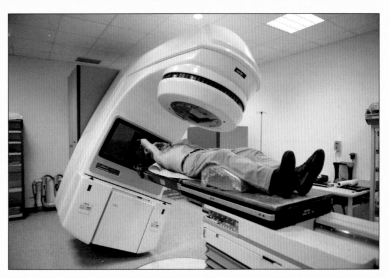

Figure 19.11 External beam radiotherapy device.

● Brachytherapy, where a sealed source is placed onto or into the skin (like the treatment for sarcoids).

● Unsealed source radiotherapy, where an unsealed source is usually swallowed or injected into the body.

Questions

5 For each of the following forms of radiotherapy suggest and explain which radioisotope(s) you would choose:
  a external beam radiotherapy
  b brachytherapy
  c unsealed source radiotherapy

6 Explain what safety precautions a specialist radiotherapy nurse would have to take if treating a patient using external beam radiotherapy.

continued...

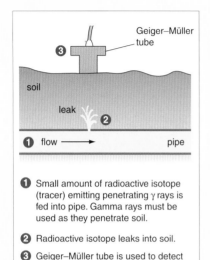

① Small amount of radioactive isotope (tracer) emitting penetrating γ rays is fed into pipe. Gamma rays must be used as they penetrate soil.

② Radioactive isotope leaks into soil.

③ Geiger–Müller tube is used to detect radiation and position of leak.

Figure 19.12 Using a radioactive tracer to detect a leak in an underground pipeline.

Leak detection

Any leak in an underground oil, gas or sewer pipe can cause a lot of pollution. If a leak is suspected, a radioactive tracer can be put into the pipeline. The radiotracer will leak out into the surroundings where there is a crack. The radioisotope will accumulate in the soil around the leak. The operator, using a Geiger counter, walks or rides over the pipeline looking for a place where the activity is higher than normal.

Figure 19.13 Operators on surface scanning for leak.

Questions

7 Which radioisotopes would you use for leak detection?

8 Why is it important that radiosotopes used in leak detection have short half-lives?

Thickness control

Sheet materials such as aluminium foil, paper, polythene and other plastic materials are made at high speed. The raw materials are passed between rollers that roll them into continuous long flat sheets. A Geiger counter in the machine measures the amount of beta radiation passing through the material.

The thicker the sheet, the less radiation will pass through to the detector, and the automatic system 'feeds back' to the rollers moving them slightly closer. This information is used to keep the sheets at the correct thickness. Beta sources are the most useful because of their penetrating ability. Gamma rays are not stopped at all by such thin sheets of these materials, and alpha particles are stopped even by a very thin sheet.

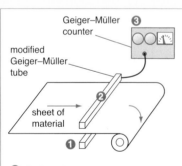

① Radioactive source emitting less penetrating beta radiation.

② Long, modified Geiger–Müller tube detects radiation penetrating the sheet of material.

③ Geiger–Müller counter measures radiation level (the thicker the sheet, the lower the reading). Information is fed back to adjust the thickness of the material if necessary.

Figure 19.14 Thickness control using radioactive materials.

Questions

9 Why are beta sources used for thickness control applications?

10 State with a reason which radioisotope you would choose for use in a thickness control machine. How would you arrange this source under the sheet?

11 Why is it important that the Geiger counter is long enough to stretch across the whole sheet?

Checking metal welds

Bridges, boilers, ships, submarines, pipelines and oil refineries are just some of many structures where sheets of thick steel are welded together. In many cases, a poor weld would be disastrous. Gamma ray sources and detectors are used to check the quality of the weld.

Questions

12 Which radioisotopes would you use for metal weld detection? Explain your answer.

13 What precautions would the operator need to take when analysing a metal weld?

14 Why would α and β radioisotopes be unsuitable for this application?

Sterilising to kill harmful bacteria

Medical instruments, such as scalpels and forceps, are placed in a package and sterilised using gamma radiation. Any harmful bacteria on the instruments and the inside of the package are killed. The ionising power of the γ rays kills the cells of the bacteria. Other products which are sterilised this way include baby powder, cosmetics and contact lens solution. No chemicals are added to the products. They can be sterilised in their packaging. It makes them very safe to use. They do not become radioactive because the γ rays are highly penetrating and pass straight through the packaging and the products they are sterilising.

Questions

15 Explain which radioisotopes you could use for a machine that sterilises medical instruments.

16 Why is it important that the sterilising machine is surrounded by a thick lead shield?

Smoke alarms

Every house should have at least two smoke alarms in place.

Discussion Point

Some types of food are treated in the same way. Strawberries, onions, potatoes and spices can all be sterilised in this way. By killing the bacteria on the food products they can have a substantially longer shelf-life. Would you like to eat irradiated strawberries?

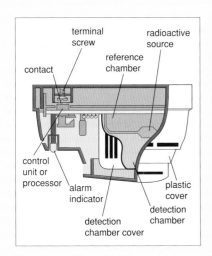

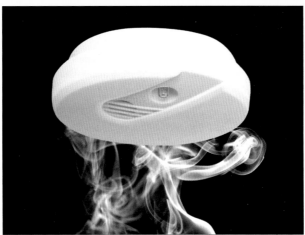

Figure 19.15 The inside of a smoke alarm and its outward appearance.

They have saved many lives. Each smoke alarm contains a tiny amount of a radioactive isotope. The source emits alpha particles which ionise the air in the alarm. This means that a small current flows. If smoke gets into the alarm it stops the current, and this switches on the loudspeaker circuit.

Questions

17 Explain why americium-241 would be a good choice for the radioisotope in a smoke detector.

18 Why doesn't a smoke alarm need a lead shield around it?

Using radioactive decay

Radiation is a peculiar thing – on the one hand it is highly dangerous, causing cells to die or mutate, killing whole organisms in large doses, yet on the other hand it has lots of different uses, many of which are medical and highly beneficial to us. The trick, of course, is to know about the properties of the different forms of radiation and the radioisotopes and use them in safe and controlled ways to our benefit. Unfortunately, uncontrolled exposure to radioactive decay is very dangerous, and even in the most safety conscious and controlled industry of nuclear power, no-one can predict the catastrophic effects of a 14 metre high tsunami on a nearby nuclear reactor, as happened in March 2011 in Japan.

Figure 19.16 Damaged Fukushima reactor.

Chapter summary

○ Radioactive decay is a random event, governed by the laws of probability. Radioactive decay can be modelled by rolling a large collection of dice, tossing a large number of coins or using a suitably programmed spreadsheet.

○ The half-life is the length of time it takes for half the atoms in the sample to decay; this is a constant for a particular element. Half-lives vary between different radioactive elements from seconds to billions of years.

○ The activity of a sample of isotope can be plotted against time on a graph, and from this the half-life of that isotope can be measured. The graph is called a radioactive decay graph.

○ The unit of radioactive decay is the becquerel, Bq. 1 Bq is 1 radioactive decay per second.

○ Carbon-14 is a naturally occurring radioactive isotope of carbon. It emits ß particles with a half-life of 5370 years. By measuring the proportion of carbon-14 to the usual isotope carbon-12, organic objects up to around 60 000 years old can be dated.

○ Alpha particles are helium nuclei so have a charge of +2. They can penetrate a few centimetres in air, but are stopped by a thin layer of skin. Because of their high ionising power (they have a strong positive charge), they can cause a lot of biological damage if they get inside you.

○ Beta particles are made up of electrons so have a charge of −1. They can travel about 15 cm in air, through several centimetres of flesh or through a few centimetres of aluminium or perspex. They can cause radiation burns.

○ Gamma radiation is uncharged electromagnetic rays. Gamma rays penetrate through material very easily and can travel through several centimetres of lead. They can cause radiation burns and there may be delayed effects that develop later such as cataracts in the eyes and cancer.

○ The characteristics of the different forms of radioactive decay mean that they are useful for different purposes, for example medical uses such as radio-imaging and radiotherapy.

Nuclear power?

Discussion Points

There are lots of resources online that show the possible effects of the La Palma mega-tsunami. You might like to try:
www.guardian.co.uk/flash/cumbre_vieja_tsunami.swf

1   Do you think that the potential for natural disaster outweighs the need for secure, large-scale, carbon-neutral electricity?

2   Global warming or nuclear disaster – which is worse in your view?

Do we want to build more nuclear power stations? On the one hand, nuclear power goes a great way towards generating large quantities of 'on-demand', carbon-neutral electricity, but on the other hand, the events of 11 March 2011, when a 8.9 magnitude earthquake 400 km north-east of Tokyo triggered a 14 m tsunami wave to hit the shore at the Fukushima Nuclear Power Plant, have made the decision to build new reactors in the UK a much more difficult proposition. However, in the UK, the largest recorded earthquake was estimated to be of magnitude 5.5, causing slight building damage when it took place in 1580. In the 'worst case scenario' a 900 m high 'mega-tsunami', caused by the potential collapse of the volcano on La Palma in the Canary Islands, would only result in a 5 m tsunami on the south coast of England. This would still cause a great deal of damage, but would be unlikely to affect any of the UK's reactors significantly.

Figure 20.1 The Japanese tsunami wave in 2011.

Where does nuclear power come from?

You saw in GCSE Science that atoms are made up of very small positively charged nuclei with electrons orbiting the nucleus.

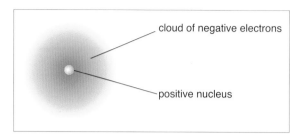

Figure 20.2 Model of the structure of the atom.

Figure 20.3 A helium atom.

You have also seen in Chapter 8 of this book that **nuclei** are made up of two types of particle: positively charged **protons** and neutral **neutrons**. Collectively these particles are called **nucleons**, as they are particles that exist in nuclei. Scientists have a shorthand way of writing the constituents of nuclei called the $^A_Z X$ **notation**. **A** is called the **nucleon number** or **mass number** and is the number of protons + number of neutrons in the nucleus. **Z** is called the **proton number** (usually called the atomic number by chemists) and **X** is the **atomic symbol** (from the Periodic Table).

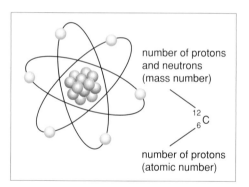

Figure 20.4 A carbon atom.

In a nuclear reactor, the fuel that is used is uranium (usually mined as low concentration uranium ore in places like Kazakhstan, Canada and Australia). The uranium in uranium ore consists of two main isotopes – uranium-238, written as $^{238}_{92}U$ and uranium-235, written as $^{235}_{92}U$. Both are forms of uranium as they both have the same number of protons in their nucleus (Z = 92), but they have different nucleon numbers (238 and 235), and so they have different numbers of neutrons.

In uranium-238, A = 238 and Z = 92, so the number of neutrons is 238 – 92 = 146

and in uranium-235, A = 235, Z = 92, so number of neutrons is 235 – 92 = 143.

Isotopes are atoms of the same element, having the same number of protons, but they have **different numbers of neutrons**.

Uranium has 26 known isotopes, ranging from U-217 to U-242, although none are stable all are radioactive, and some, like U-235 and U-238, have very long half-lives.

Uranium-238, $^{238}_{92}U$, is radioactive and decays by emitting an alpha particle, $^{4}_{2}He$, into thorium-234, $^{234}_{90}Th$. This can be summarised by a nuclear equation:

$$^{238}_{92}U \rightarrow {}^{234}_{90}Th + {}^{4}_{2}He$$

The general nuclear equation for alpha particle decay is:

$$^{A}_{Z}X \rightarrow {}^{A-4}_{Z-2}Y + {}^{4}_{2}He$$

The thorium-234 formed by the decay of uranium-238 in a nuclear reactor is also radioactive and decays by emitting beta particles, $^{0}_{-1}e$. The nuclear equation for this decay is:

$$^{234}_{90}Th \rightarrow {}^{234}_{91}Pa + {}^{0}_{-1}e$$

The general nuclear equation for beta particle decay is:

$$^{A}_{Z}X \rightarrow {}^{A}_{Z+1}Y + {}^{0}_{-1}e$$

QUESTIONS

1 Write nuclear equations for the following decays:

   a uranium-235, $^{235}_{92}U$, also an alpha particle emitter, decaying into thorium-231, $^{231}_{90}Th$.

   b carbon-14, $^{14}_{6}C$, is a beta emitter, decaying into nitrogen-14, $^{14}_{7}N$.

2 Use a Periodic Table or a Table of Nuclides (try: http://en.wikipedia.org/wiki/Table_of_nuclides_(complete)) to write nuclear equations to determine the decay product of the following isotopes:

   a alpha emitters:

     i americium-241

     ii polonium-210

     iii radon-222

     iv radium-226

     v plutonium-236

   b beta emitters:

     i hydrogen-3 (tritium)

     ii phosphorus-32

     iii nickel-63

     iv strontium-90

     v sodium-24

Nuclear fission

All current nuclear reactors use the process of nuclear fission to produce their primary source of heat energy – the word 'fission' means 'breaking up'. The main isotope used in nuclear reactors to provide the heat energy is uranium-235, $^{235}_{92}U$, which is radioactive and decays via alpha decay into thorium-231, $^{231}_{90}Th$. However, in a nuclear reactor, the U-235 nuclei can be broken up into 'daughter' nuclei, if they are bombarded by **slow-moving neutrons** – this process, called nuclear fission, also produces more neutrons, which themselves, in turn, can produce the fission of other U-235 nuclei, and so on, starting a process called a **chain reaction**.

During the process of nuclear fission, each U-235 nucleus that undergoes decay emits 3.2×10^{-11} J of energy. This does not sound like very much, until you do the sums and find out that 1 kg of U-235 produces 83 000 000 000 000 J of energy (83 terrajoules or 83 TJ).

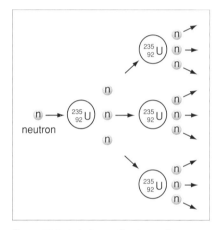

Figure 20.5 A chain reaction in uranium-235.

Discussion Points

1 You do the maths: 1 atom of U-235 has a mass of 3.9×10^{-25} kg. How many atoms of U-235 are there in 1 kg? If each atom's nucleus can emit 3.2×10^{-11} J of heat energy, how much heat energy could 1 kg of U-235 produce?

2 Is nuclear power from fission worth it in terms of energy? 1 kg of U-235 could produce about 83 TJ (83×10^{12} J) of energy. By comparison, 1 kg of best coal could produce 35 MJ (35×10^{6} J). How much coal would you have to burn to get the same amount of energy as 1 kg of uranium-235?

3 Are there any other considerations when comparing coal and uranium?

How does fission work?

The fission of U-235 breaks the U-235 nucleus up into two daughter nuclei, one with a nucleon number of about 137 and another with a nucleon number of about 95. On average, three neutrons are also produced, but this can be up to five or as low as one. The precise decay that any one U-235 nucleus undergoes depends upon many factors, including the speed of the incoming fission neutron. We can represent one common decay by the nuclear equation:

$$^{235}_{92}U + ^{1}_{0}n \rightarrow ^{144}_{56}Ba + ^{89}_{36}Kr + 3^{1}_{0}n + energy$$

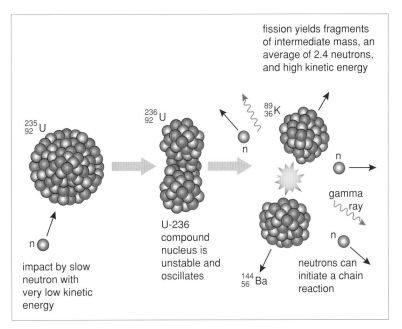

Figure 20.6 Uranium-235 decay.

3 Use a Periodic Table or a Table of Nuclides to write nuclear equations to summarise the following fission reactions inside a nuclear fuel rod, occurring from the fission of uranium-235 from one neutron. The fission products are:

a xenon-140, strontium-94 and two neutrons

b rubidium-90, caesium-144 and two neutrons

c lanthanum-146, bromine-87 and three neutrons.

Reactor engineering

The nuclear fission process is only possible if the neutrons that are released from the fission of uranium-235 are moving slowly enough. If the neutrons are moving too fast they will not cause fission. The slow-moving neutrons are called thermal neutrons – the amount of energy in the moving neutrons is similar to the amount of energy in the vibrating atoms in the fuel rod. In order to slow down the fast-moving neutrons produced by the nuclear fission process, the fuel rods in the reactor are surrounded by a material called a moderator. Over 80% of the world's nuclear reactors use water as the moderator (these are called pressurised water reactors or PWRs), with about 20% using graphite rods (graphite is a physical form of carbon). The advantage of using water as a moderator is that it can also act as the coolant and the mechanism of heat transfer for the reactor. In the event of loss of coolant, the nuclear chain reaction stops (the neutrons are moving too fast), but the reactor overheats; this is one of the things that happened at the Fukushima Nuclear Plant following the tsunami of March 2011.

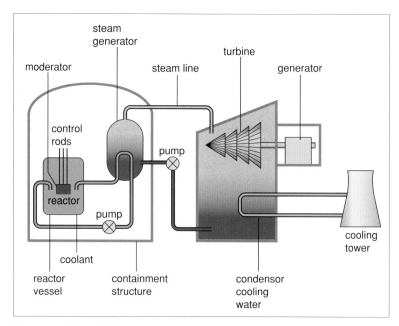

Figure 20.7 Pressurised water reactor.

The whole nuclear fission process can be completely stopped or speeded up or slowed down by controlling the number of thermal neutrons inside the fuel rods. In a nuclear reactor this is achieved by inserting neutron-absorbing rods, called **control rods**, into the spaces between the fuel rods. Materials such as boron, cadmium and hafnium are commonly used to make control rods. All modern reactors have simple, 'fail-safe' mechanisms built into their systems so that, if a fault occurs, the control rods automatically drop down into the reactor, shutting off the chain reaction. Moving the control rods down into the reactor slows the reaction down (or completely stops it) by absorbing more of the thermal neutrons, and moving them up speeds up the reaction by absorbing fewer thermal neutrons.

The safety of nuclear reactors is further improved by encasing the reactor inside a strong steel pressure vessel, and then surrounding the whole reactor vessel inside a containment structure made of concrete. The combined effect of the pressure vessel and the containment structure is to prevent any stray unwanted radioactivity from escaping from the reactor. Most of the decay products of nuclear fission are radioactive, many with extremely long half-lives (U-235 itself has a half-life of 700 million years), so it is very important that once reactor fuel rods have been used up (spent), that they are safely stored within the containment structure under water in 'cooling ponds'. This allows them to cool down safely, without their radiation escaping from the reactor building.

You can find out about how nuclear reactors work by searching online using key-words such as 'nuclear power plant' 'animation' 'applet'. Your teacher may show you one of these. How is the heat energy generated by the reactor transformed into electricity?

Figure 20.8 A nuclear cooling pond.

Once the spent fuel rods have cooled down, they can be removed to a nuclear re-processing facility such as Sellafield in Cumbria and ultimately stored deep underground.

QUESTIONS

4 What is the main fuel used in a nuclear reactor?

5 What is a 'chain reaction'?

6 Why does a nuclear reactor need a moderator?

7 How can a nuclear power station reactor be controlled?

8 Why is the reactor encased inside a steel vessel surrounded by a thick concrete containment structure?

9 Why do spent fuel rods need to be stored under water in ponds within the containment structure?

10 Draw a flow chart showing how electricity is generated by nuclear fission in a nuclear power station.

Is there another way?

The energy produced by our Sun (and other stars) is also produced by nuclear reactions.

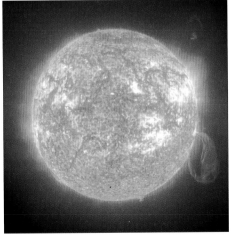

Figure 20.9 Our Sun.

In this case, the nuclear reaction involves the **fusion** (joining together) of nuclei, rather than fission. This process produces enormous amounts of energy. Remember, 1 kg of burning coal could produce 35 MJ (35×10^6 J) of heat energy. One kilogram of uranium-235 could produce 83 TJ (83×10^{12} J) of heat energy. One kilogram of hydrogen could produce 0.6 petajoules, 0.6 PJ (0.6×10^{15} J) – over 7 times as much as 1 kg of uranium-235!

Even though the Sun produces so much nuclear energy, and fuses hydrogen at a rate of over 6×10^{11} kg/s, the Sun still has enough hydrogen to keep on shining for at least another 5 thousand million years.

So, if hydrogen fusion can produce such large amounts of energy, can we develop a nuclear fusion reactor here on Earth and have endless amounts of clean, carbon-free energy? Unfortunately, this is easier said than done.

It turns out that in order to get hydrogen nuclei (protons) close enough to undergo nuclear fusion (and overcome the large force of repulsion due to their positive charge), they need to be moving at very high speed. Because hydrogen is a gas, that means very, very high temperatures and pressures; in fact, temperatures of over 15 million degrees celcius. These temperatures are easily reached inside the huge mass of stars such as the Sun, but here on Earth this temperature is very difficult to achieve, and even harder to control and keep going.

Inside the Sun, hydrogen nuclei (protons) fuse together, making nuclei of helium and a range of other fusion products including the gamma rays that produce the energy emitted by the Sun. A summary of the nuclear fusion reaction inside the core of the Sun (and most other stars) is shown below:

4 protons → helium nucleus + 2 gamma rays

$$4{}^1_1\text{H} \rightarrow {}^4_2\text{He} + 2\gamma$$

(This is actually a very simplified version of the nuclear fusion process in the Sun. It's actually called the proton-proton (pp) chain and involves several other types of particle.)

On Earth, nuclear fusion reactions have been produced involving the fusion of light elements, in particular the 'heavy' isotopes of hydrogen – deuterium (hydrogen-2, ${}^2_1\text{H}$) and tritium (hydrogen-3, ${}^3_1\text{H}$). The Joint European Torus (JET) facility at Culham near Oxford has produced nuclear fusion of these isotopes.

Figure 20.10 JET reactor.

JET has produced a peak power output of 16 MW (which is 65% of the input power) for a period of 0.5 seconds. It is hoped that the International Thermonuclear Experimental Reactor (ITER) currently under construction at Cadarche in southern France will be up and running in 2018, and will be producing 500 MW (for a 50 MW input power).

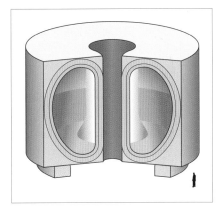

Figure 20.11 ITER tokamak.

Inside the toroidal (doughnut-shaped) 'tokamak' reactor, the deuterium and tritium nuclei are accelerated around the reactor, confined by very high magnetic fields, and heated by huge electric currents passing through the ionised gas (called a plasma). As they whizz around the reactor they collide with enough energy to undergo nuclear fusion. The nuclear fusion reaction between deuterium and tritium inside the tokamak is summarised by the nuclear equation:

$$_1^2 H + {}_1^3 H \rightarrow {}_2^4 He + {}_0^1 n$$

The neutron (and the helium nucleus) that is produced in this process is moving at very high speeds, and it is this kinetic energy that could be used as the heat source for any potential nuclear power plant. One of the problems with the current design of reactors such as JET and ITER is that the huge numbers of neutrons produced in the process can interact with the material that makes up the tokamak, making it radioactive. The whole reactor (like a fission reactor) needs to be shielded with large amounts of concrete to prevent radiation escaping into the environment.

QUESTIONS

11 What is nuclear fusion?

12 Inside the core of the Sun, what are the particles involved with nuclear fusion?

13 Why are high temperatures and pressures needed for nuclear fusion?

14 What are deuterium and tritium? How are they different to 'normal' hydrogen?

15 What is a plasma?

16 How is the plasma of deuterium and tritium confined inside a tokamak reactor?

17 How are the high temperatures generated within a tokamak reactor?

18 How could the energy of a nuclear fusion reactor be used to produce electricity?

19 Why do nuclear fusion reactors need a lot of shielding?

Discussion Point

Other rival nuclear fusion reactor designs (such as HiPER – the European **Hi**gh **P**ower laser **E**nergy **R**esearch facility) would use high powered lasers to heat a small quantity of deuterium and tritium inside a small spherical pellet. Such designs have been shown to work, producing small quantities of nuclear fusion. The trick is to get a continuous feed of fusion fuel into the laser beams in a short enough time to sustain the reaction. Use the internet to find out about nuclear fusion reactors that use lasers (the process is called Inertial Confinement Fusion or ICF). How might it compare to tokamak based reactors?

The future of energy?

What is the future of energy production for the world? Can we carry on burning fossil fuels at such an enormous rate, accelerating the greenhouse effect and global warming? In the future will the use of nuclear power increase, or have the events of March 2011 on the coast of Japan put the brakes on the nuclear fission band-wagon? By 2018 we should know the first results of the ITER nuclear fusion project, but a commercial nuclear fusion power plant is still a very long way off, and in any event the €15 billion price-tag may be just too much in the current economic conditions. One thing that we do know is that if we don't do something about it, the future could be very dark.

Chapter summary

- ○ Radioactive emissions from unstable atomic nuclei arise because of an imbalance between the numbers of protons and neutrons.
- ○ The number of protons and neutrons in an atomic nucleus is called the nucleon number or the mass number (A), and the number of protons is called the proton number (Z) (chemists usually call it the atomic number).
- ○ Different isotopes of an element all have the same number of protons in their nucleus, but they have different numbers of nucleons, and so they have different numbers of neutrons.
- ○ The nuclear symbols in the form of the $^A_Z X$ notation (where X is the atomic symbol from the Periodic Table) are useful in the context of transformations including radioactive decay, nuclear fission and nuclear fusion.
- ○ Data about nuclear symbols can be used to produce and balance nuclear equations.
- ○ The absorption of slow neutrons can induce fission of U-235 nuclei, releasing energy, and the emission of neutrons from such fission can lead to a sustainable chain reaction.
- ○ Moderator material in a nuclear reactor acts to slow down the fast-moving neutrons produced by the nuclear fission process, so that they can cause further fission.
- ○ Control rods are neutron-absorbing rods that can be moved up and down to control the number of thermal neutrons there are inside the fuel rods.
- ○ Most of the decay products of nuclear fission are radioactive, many of them with very long half-lives, so they have to be carefully stored within the containment structure of the nuclear reactor.
- ○ High energy collisions between light nuclei, especially isotopes of hydrogen, can result in fusion which releases enormous amounts of energy.
- ○ For fusion to go ahead very high temperatures are required which are difficult to achieve and control.
- ○ The problems of containment in fission and fusion reactors also include neutron and gamma shielding and pressure containment in fusion reactors.

Index

Index